C000280775

Comfort and Care
for the Critically Ill

June Cerza Kolf

Baker Books
A Division of Baker Book House Co.
Grand Rapids, Michigan 49516

Published by Baker Books
A division of Baker Book House Company
PO Box 6287, Grand Rapids, Michigan 49516-6287

ISBN: 0-8010-5257-2

Printed in the United States of America

Contents

Preface

I had finished my third book and was not working on anything in particular when my friend Bonnie approached me.

"The doctors have just told my aunt there is nothing more that can be done to cure her. They have, in essence, sent her home to die. Is there a book I can get that will help her in the days ahead?" she asked.

I sadly shook my head, "No."

"Well, maybe you should write one," Bonnie said.

A few days later Carol Levy, the executive director of our local chapter of the American Cancer Society called to ask me to visit an acquaintance of hers who had just received a terminal diagnosis.

"I wish I had a book I could give to people who are going through the process of dying. They have so many questions and they need some answers," she said.

When the third person in one week asked me about a similar book, I realized I was being given a job to do. I headed back to my computer and while God gave me the words my hands did the typing.

I believe this and my other books are the result of a task the Lord has given me. I also believe he makes me aware of these tasks with messages from my friends and family. However, I'm afraid I don't always listen as closely as I should, but the Lord, in his infinite wisdom, simply perseveres until he gets through to me.

I would like to dedicate this book, in gratitude, to all those special people who listen closely when God sends them information for me. Thank you, dear friends, for passing those messages on—over and over and over again—until I finally hear them.

Throughout this book I will be referring to the person with the terminal diagnosis as "the patient." I will use the generic term "he" to make for smoother reading. The person who cares for the patient when he is at home is called "the caregiver."

Acknowledgments

My special appreciation goes to the following people who so generously gave both their time and professional advice to help create this book.

LeeRoy Halley
Carol Levy, R.N.
Pastor Ron Salsbury
Judge Richard E. Spann

Part One
The Patient

Introduction

When I was born, people were happy and smiling.
I was the only one crying.
When I died, people were sad and crying.
I was the only one happy and smiling.

—Hospice of the East San Gabriel Valley

A doctor walks slowly into his office with his head down, his demeanor clearly stating defeat. He sits down behind his desk and looks in the direction of the young woman sitting across from him, but he avoids her eyes.

Clearing his throat, he says, "All the test results are finally in. It looks like you have a very aggressive strain of lung cancer that won't respond to any further treatment."

Debbie's brow furrows as she tries to assimilate the information.

"What do you mean?" she asks softly.

"Well," the doctor answers, still avoiding her eyes, "I'm afraid there is nothing more that can be done."

Debbie finally asks, "Does that mean I'm going to die?"

"It's very probable," the doctor says, and then his eyes, filled with tears, meet hers.

Many times life-threatening illnesses can be treated or put into remission for long periods of time. Also, in certain cases, experimental programs may be appropriate. I will not be addressing those situations. This book is for patients who have been given a terminal prognosis with no suggestion of recovery or remission.

After Debbie's physician tells her there is nothing more that can be done for her medically, what can she do? What are her choices? How many more opinions should she seek? Are there experimental programs she can look into? How will she come to terms with such devastating news? What can her family and friends do to help? How can she spend her remaining time so that it is as meaningful and productive as possible?

There are no pat answers for any of these questions, but there are guidelines that have proved successful for others. Even after the medical experts have reached the conclusion that a patient is medically incurable, it does not mean that a person needs to be without hope. A medical opinion is just that, *an opinion,* and it can be overridden by God at any time. Never stop looking for a miracle. The human body has marvelous recuperative powers and even without a miracle life can still have quality. The patient and his family can be well cared for physically, emotionally, and spiritually in whatever time remains. It can be a special period of time.

This book is divided into two distinct sections, one intended for the patient and one for the people who are caring for the patient (the caregivers). Much of the information is the same, but it is offered from different perspectives to allow for the best teamwork possible. Reading the material from both perspectives is not required, but it might be helpful. The more familiar everyone is with the subject matter, the easier it will be to deal with all aspects of the terminal diagnosis.

1

The Physical Aspect

Along with a terminal diagnosis comes the process of facing our own and our loved one's mortality. Without realizing it, we are all in the process of dying from the day we are born. However, when a devastating illness hits, we must face it more actively because a tentative time limit is set on life.

Acceptance

Acceptance comes about mainly as a result of thinking, talking, and praying about the situation. During this time following acceptance we can actively participate in the process of dying. When a person denies the truth there is no chance of reaching acceptance. Like touching a gaping wound, go at it slowly. Attempt only what you can handle each day. Talk to a trusted friend; let your tears express what cannot be put into words. The information in this book may help bring about acceptance along with practical tasks to make the days ahead easier.

The final days in a person's life can be a time of peace, sharing, and joy, or a time of struggle, tears, and pain. Death, like any other life experience, is what we make of it for ourselves and our loved ones. We may not be able to control the illness, but we *can* control the atmosphere that surrounds us. We can fill the time with feelings of hope or bitterness. We can form a community of healing, if not for the body, then for the emotions and spirit. We can enjoy our loved ones or we can strike out at them in anger. We can appreciate the physical care we are receiving or we can lash out with harsh demands. The quality of our life, whether in sickness or in health, depends on us.

If you have not already been praying to be healed, begin to do so right now. Prayers are answered in a variety of ways, just as healing can occur in a variety of ways. Healing may come in the form of a healed body or in healed relationships. Your prayers may be answered with an inner presence of peace that comes with acceptance or with the ultimate healing that comes only in death.

I pray the following information will open avenues that may be blocked and clear the way for an easier journey.

Possible Reactions

Usually the first feeling that follows a terminal diagnosis is shock. Debbie will probably return home in a daze while she tries to grasp the devastating information she has just received. Shock, nature's anesthetic, acts as a cushion against intense pain. Shock wears off gradually as the mind becomes able to accept the fateful news.

Along with or following closely behind shock will be denial. Thoughts of *there must be some mistake* and *this can't be possible* will probably fill Debbie's mind. As she talks about and thinks about her illness, little by little she will begin to realize she is facing a life-threatening situation.

In the very beginning, the best remedy for working through shock to a point of acceptance is to talk about the prognosis. As Debbie hears the words and expresses her feelings, reality will gradually creep in. You may be experiencing the same feelings.

In addition to shock and denial when you are told your illness is not curable, you may be struck with agonizing fear—fear of the future, fear of no longer being in control. Dread engulfs you like a heavy, wet blanket, threatening to suffocate you with every breath. Your stomach churns and you keep wishing you would wake up from this terrorizing nightmare. Unfortunately, you are already awake and what you are experiencing is not a nightmare.

It is real life, suddenly appearing in stark black and white. You are wide-awake, asking repeatedly "Why me?" and "Why now?" Rarely is a person ready to face the fact that life here on earth may be coming to an end. There is always a reason why the timing is not right. There are always things we want to live a little longer to see or do. Possibly you have just started a successful career or had a baby. You are not ready to die. You bargain with God, make promises, do anything to buy some extra time, while your insides are clutched tight with fear.

Although my own father, in his eighties, lived two years after his terminal diagnosis, we wanted to hang on to him an extra two weeks so that he could celebrate his fifty-third wedding anniversary with Mom. We forgot to be thankful for the two extra years we were granted with Dad and instead felt cheated out of the two weeks.

Human beings hold very tightly to earthly ties. We think of death as a thief rather than a natural conclusion to life. We are not eager to move on to the unknown. We want to get our children raised and then we want to be able to hold our grandchildren. We want to just finish this one book we're writing, but when it is complete we suddenly have an idea for another one—*just one more thing, Lord*—always one more.

I once heard a preacher say that for the Christian death is a mere relocation. A true statement, but not much consolation to the person who is being relocated before he is ready or without his vote. By talking about your fears instead of repressing them, a point of acceptance will be easier to reach. With acceptance can come quality time that is spoken of as the "final gift."

The first time a terminal patient verbalized that his illness was his last earthly gift from God, I was shocked. *Wait a minute! How could a devastating illness be a gift?* But with time and more experience, I began to understand. People who die suddenly do not have the opportunity to get their affairs in order. They are denied a final farewell, the distribution of material items, the mending of broken relationships, the expression of love, and the straightening out of legal and financial matters. But worst of all, sometimes sudden death comes before a person's spiritual life is in order. Along with a terminal diagnosis comes an opportunity to finalize matters in all areas.

"The period of time following a terminal diagnosis can be a time of great love, of sharing and of caring," writes Lois Wyse about the days following her husband's terminal diagnosis.

And, as we do from all of life's crises, we learned. We learned that people can be very tender and caring in expressing concern. We were touched by the calls and letters, the flowers and plants, the books and balloons, the candy and fruit. . . . In that sweet summer of our marriage, we held each other close.[1]

What a waste it would be to not make the most of this time! Take this gift and use it to become closer to God. Change "Why me?" to "How can I use this time to its fullest?" Spend your time getting better acquainted with the Lord so that when you approach the end of life's road you will be met by a good friend instead of a stranger. Think of God as a loving father who does not wish illness onto his children. Instead, illness comes from living in an imperfect world while the father stands on the sidelines, hurting desperately, ready to offer support through insufferable times.

By working together with loved ones the process of dying can become a special part of life, a time of deep caring which will make the passage natural and peaceful. "With acceptance comes a feeling of victory, a feeling of peace, of serenity, of positive submission to things we cannot change."[2]

This final journey can be a time of forming lasting memories and receiving gentle care. Think of this time as a unique period of preparation, for along with the anguish of having to face a terminal diagnosis comes the opportunity to prepare for death. The time when a person is ill need not be wasted. It can be quality time spent with loved ones sharing special moments that you never had time for previously. Even though completely debilitated, Vera showed me that this was possible.

When I met Vera I was overwhelmed by her condition. She could do absolutely nothing for herself physically and was entirely dependent on her family for her total care. As we talked I was surprised by her cheerful nature. She laughed as she said, "I bet you can't guess what I do all day long?" I had to admit I could not.

"I spend all day praying. I pray for my friends who have time only for quick prayers said on the run. I pray for my family. I pray for our community, and for world peace. I pray for everybody and everything. I never run out. I'll be praying for you, too, now that I've met you."

She told me that when she had been well she never had much time for prayer.

"So you see, out of my illness has come some good. For the first time in my life I'm spending quality time with God and at the same time I'm doing something important for my family and friends."

Her family told me that they could feel her prayer support as they went about their daily tasks. They let Vera know their particular needs so she could pray about them and they showered her with appreciation which made her feel worthy and useful.

Medical Care

A terminal diagnosis is given when the medical profession has no more options to offer. The following information is meant to help during this phase of illness.

Stopping active treatment even on a terminal patient is a most difficult task for health care personnel. Because people in the medical profession are trained in curing, it is an almost insurmountable task for many doctors to simply let nature run its course. Doctors have been trained to heal. To handle their profession, they must be self-assured. The very confidence that allows them to perform surgery and do their various daily tasks is the same confidence that will stand in the way when they have to give up aggressive treatment. To some, it feels like failure. Therefore, it is up to patients to make their desires known if they wish to stop treatment that is not going to make them better.

Do not misunderstand. I am grateful that doctors do not give up easily. When I am ill I want to know that their training has them doing everything humanly possible to make me well. But when they can no longer cure me or improve my condition, I do not want them to be experimenting and prolonging a meaningless existence. I want their honesty, and I want to be sent home to die as comfortably and as peacefully as possible.

Even after aggressive treatment of the disease is halted, it is still necessary to be under a physician's care for treatment of the symptoms and for comfort measures. Simply be aware of the difference.

Many people do not realize that our physical well-being is in our own hands. Even when we seek medical attention, the final decision is our own. We can always refuse tests, medication, or treatment. Usually, this would be foolish. If we desire to have our good health reinstated and a doctor has the knowledge to bring that about, we should follow his instructions carefully. However, if we feel uncomfortable about the physician's course of action, or we seem to be making little or no progress, it is perfectly permissible and advisable to seek a second or even a third opinion.

Following a terminal diagnosis many decisions about medical care must be faced. You cannot simply go to bed and rest until you get well. You must be actively involved in your medical care. It is absolutely vital for both patient and caregiver to be knowledgeable about all medical decisions and the reasoning behind them. Even if you are in the hospital, try to fully understand what is being done so that if and when you go home follow-up care will be easier.

For instance, do not just swallow a pill when it is handed to you. Ask for the name of the drug and what it is for. When you fill a prescription, ask the pharmacist for brochures and extra information. If you are not personally informed you cannot participate in what is going on.

Do as much research into the disease as you are physically able to do. When you leave the doctor's office or hospital, find books on your particular illness and learn everything you can about it. Ask about the progression of your disease and gather statistics. Call the "800" hotlines for your particular illness and ask for written material. Some of these telephone numbers are listed in the back of this book. Find out if there are support groups in your area. If the diagnosis is cancer, call your local American Cancer Society and ask for printed material.

By keeping a close watch, if you choose to seek other medical opinions, you will be able to tell the doctor, "I take 100 mg. of Dilantin twice a day for seizures," instead of, "Oh, I take a tiny white capsule twice a day for something." It makes a big difference! Ask questions about your treatment plan. You have a right to know what is going on and what the doctors are planning to do to your body.

Talking with Your Doctor

Often a doctor continues treatment for the mental well-being of the patient. Let your doctor know your desires. Tell him if you choose the cessation of an experimental treatment. Let him know if you are more interested in quality or quantity of life. Be honest about your needs and feelings. Doctors almost always respect a patient's wishes when they are aware of them. Often both patient and doctor play pretend games to make it easier for each other. Try not to get yourself into this situation. If you are unable to confide in your doctor or health care team or feel uncomfortable talking to them about personal matters, it may be time to find new people with whom you can be more at ease.

The following list will help you to communicate more effectively with your doctor.

1. *Decide how much information you desire.* Some people deal better with a situation when they know every detail; others prefer to judge their health by the way they are feeling. Unless your physician has known you for a long time, he may not know your preferences. Therefore, it is up to you to clarify them at the start. For instance, opposite extremes would be, "I wish to have full knowledge of my condition, no matter how bad it is." Or, "Don't give me any bad news. I want to have only positive information about my health."

2. *Understand any information you are given.* Often when we are distressed we do not hear all of the message we are being given. If you are confused, ask your doctor to repeat the information. This may also be necessary if you do not understand the medical jargon he is using.

3. *Ask specific questions.* Take a list if necessary. Possible questions are:

   What exactly is my condition?
   How will it be treated?
   What are my options?

What are the benefits and side effects of my
    options?
What are the risks?
What can I expect in the course of my illness?

4. *Ask when the best time is to telephone if you have further questions.* Most doctors have a particular time when they will take telephone calls. It is best to be familiar with their schedules.

Feel confident about the care you are receiving and comfortable with the providers. Be sure you understand your condition. You must feel at ease conversing with your health care team. It is important to feel a bond of caring as you begin what could be a long process of dealing with each other.

How Long?

Naturally you will want to know how much time you have left. The most unanswerable question ever asked is, "How long do I have?" Statisticians give averages and doctors state odds, but if someone simply pulled a number out of a hat or flipped a coin it would probably be just as accurate. Man can give his opinion, but it is merely an educated guess.

The lack of a definite time span is difficult for us to accept. Habitually, we live on a schedule. We have clocks and calendars, routines and agendas. We want to know what time something will happen and on what day of the week so we can mark it on our precious calendars. We check our watches all day long.

Then along comes a day when we are told an event will occur, but we have no date or time. It is foreign to us to live with an indefinite deadline. First we are expected to accept the unacceptable news, and then we are expected to make plans for an unknown date. Is it any wonder the concept is so difficult to grasp? All previous plans must be put on hold. Instead of dinner dates, we now have appointments with specialists. We go for medical treatments instead of shopping and we do not dare make vacation plans for next summer. We are forced to live with no schedule and no certainties. This is one of the most difficult concepts to accept following a terminal diagnosis. Even on good days we are waiting for the proverbial second shoe to fall.

The gift people talk about which comes with a terminal diagnosis arrives in the form of acceptance at having no time frame to work within. You somehow come to grips that the second shoe will fall, but you no longer wait tensely for it to happen. You begin to adapt to living with short-range instead of long-range plans and you confirm that there are no certainties in life. The sum total of these changes in lifestyle can be quite liberating. Once acceptance takes place, time no longer matters. An event of enormous proportions is about to happen in your life and you must be ready at all times.

As a result of my work I am constantly being reminded that I am a terminal being as well. I sometimes find myself looking at a patient thinking, "I could die before she does." I am very aware of how fragile and temporary life is, not just for those diagnosed with a terminal illness, but for every single one of us. Nevertheless, it is unlikely that the rest of us will take being terminal as seriously as do those with a life-threatening illness.

A terminal diagnosis should be taken seriously. However, all of us have heard of both miraculous healings and sudden unexpected deaths. I have come to acknowledge that where life and death are concerned there are no sure things. I knew a woman who was given six months to live, but who refused to die until every one of her four children had graduated from college. She had to hang on for sixteen years, but much to her physician's surprise, she did. I have also seen people pass a yearly physical with flying colors and die the next week of a massive coronary. Because there are no sure things in life, we must all live every day to its fullest.

One of my patients took me thoroughly by surprise. I spent a pleasant afternoon with Grace, who had terminal lung cancer. We talked about her trip to the mall the previous weekend and laughed as she complained about the smog hanging over California that day.

"Nobody believes me when I tell them I'm allergic to smog. I can feel it when I breathe. I've told the doctors it's what gave me lung cancer," she stated, "but they just laugh." Then, with a merry twinkle in her eyes she laughed and said, "I want my grave marker to say, 'See, I told you I was allergic to smog!'"

Grace's five children hovered around her in a house that was filled with love. Her cheeks were rosy and other than a deep, croupy cough, Grace looked healthier than I felt after my recent bout with the stomach flu. I went home smiling, feeling she was going to get well.

"You won't surprise me with this miracle," I told God. "I can feel it already."

The telephone call came at midnight that same night with the news that Grace had died. God had surprised me after all. I thought about Grace's rosy cheeks and hearty laughter as I shed tears for her children.

At the same time I was seeing Grace, I was seeing Eula Jean. Eula Jean had cervical cancer. Following extensive surgery she received radiation treatments and massive chemotherapy. I asked her doctor if these drastic procedures were going to cure her.

"Absolutely not. There isn't a chance," he told me sadly. But Eula Jean was insisting on every possible treatment even though the doctor had been perfectly honest with her.

"God wants to heal me and I have to do my part," she told me in her sweet little voice. As I watched her condition deteriorate, I hurt for her. I kept fretting that she was putting herself through all this agony for nothing. I sighed and shook my head but I continued to pray. Eula Jean had asked me to pray for her on my first visit. She had friends praying in churches all over town.

"I've got the Catholics and the Methodists and the Baptists praying!" she would giggle. "I've got all the bases covered and I'm ready for a home run."

I was afraid her home run and mine were not going to be the same.

It was not that Eula Jean was afraid to die. She loved the Lord. She simply felt in her heart that it was not the right time. I tried to support her decision to continue treatment as she grew weaker and had to go into a convalescent home. Eventually she had tubes taking care of all her bodily functions and she was being given continual oxygen. Her bald head was covered with a stocking cap and she shivered day and night. She could no longer eat or speak, but she would smile weakly whenever I visited.

During this time my father became very ill so I left town to help take care of him. I was gone for over a month. I did not see Eula Jean right away after I returned home, but I received reports from our office. Each time our nurses visited they saw progress. Without a doubt, Eula Jean was getting better. Six years later Eula Jean is still alive and well. She is actively working with the patients in the convalescent home where she lives. She is an advocate for patients' rights and she loves and cares for the other patients from her wheelchair.

Her eyes twinkle when she tells me, "See, I told you God wasn't through with me yet!"

When patients receive a terminal diagnosis they must, of course, consider the facts, but it seems to do no harm to go with what the heart is saying. Eula Jean's heart told her she would get well. Of course, every patient wants to believe he or she will be the exception—the miracle case. Hope can work in one's favor, but it would be foolish to count on it. I suggest to my patients and their families that they check out all the facts and then settle down to live each day to the fullest, ready for a miracle, but not banking on it exclusively. I suggest they get their affairs in order, but plan for either outcome.

Either way, the time following a terminal diagnosis can be good. Each day takes on new meaning and importance when time does not loom ahead of us in endless years. Long-term plans now become short-term plans or are set aside entirely. Priorities change. Keeping the house clean becomes less important than sitting with a loved one, watching the sky turn amber as the sun sets behind a mountain.

Pain and Treatment

Often the fear of pain interferes with a peaceful existence. *Coming Home* is a book that addresses the issue of pain from an interesting standpoint, stating,

> The most consistently voiced fear about dying and death is physical pain, particularly of cancer. . . . Each of us

reacts differently to pain because it is experienced by the whole individual, physically, emotionally, mentally and spiritually. So a unique pain relief program must be developed for each individual. . . . Even as we move to relieve pain, we need to be aware of its purpose. Pain is neither good nor bad; it's simply a messenger that tells us something in our life is not working or needs attention or that we're resisting what is happening. It's pain that moves us to leave behind old patterns and ways of being that no longer work. The more a dying person clings to the body, the more pain she or he experiences.[3]

I am a migraine headache sufferer so pain is no stranger in my life. My father also was a migraine sufferer. He experienced very little pain during his final illness and I often wonder if it is because he had learned how to live with pain. Migraine sufferers learn how to relax their bodies and not fight pain. They learn how to focus on something other than their pain to serve as a distraction. One of my favorite tricks is to place an ice bag on my throbbing temple and sing hymns mentally while the pain subsides. I have found through experimentation that with or without pain medication the results are exactly the same, so I no longer use drugs but rather depend on other methods of pain relief.

Most people are not accustomed to living with pain. The more foreign it is to a person the more frightening it will be. Try not to fight pain, but do not feel it is necessary to suffer in silence either. Letting your caregiver or health professional know that you are having pain is not considered a weakness. It is necessary for them to know so they can help you. Strive for the greatest relief with the least grogginess. Drugs can be used together, alternated, or given in different forms. Experiment under a health care professional's direction to find the best treatment, with or without drugs, in your particular situation.

Hospice nurses feel strongly that addiction is not to be a concern. If addictive drugs are being used they are being given in conjunction with the severity of the pain. Consider them a necessity. Do not suffer with intense pain because of the fear of addiction. Pain relief, at this time, is of utmost importance. If the pain were to disappear, the addiction could be dealt with and reversed at that time.

Frederick J. Meyers, M.D., hospice medical director and associate professor in the Division of Hematology and Oncology at the U.C. Davis School of Medicine, wrote in a paper,

> In spite of advancing technology in pain management patients are not receiving the relief from pain that some would expect. There is a gap in the education of health care professionals in dealing with hospice centers. Most health care professionals do not understand how to use narcotics appropriately in the care of the terminally ill and they don't understand their pain. They have unfounded concerns on addiction and overdosing.[4]

Discuss any medication questions or concerns with your physician or pharmacist and be sure adequate pain control is maintained at all times. Seek new health care professionals if you are dissatisfied with the way your pain is being handled.

Look into non-medication methods of pain relief that are gaining in popularity. There are pain control clinics, people who specialize in various methods of pain relief, and books written on the subject. Relaxation techniques, distraction, and massage have all proven to be good aids to lessen pain. An entirely new field using creativity for pain relief is evolving.

The Fall 1991 issue of *Thanatos* magazine[5] defines creative arts as music, literature, and dance, cassette tapes and poetry readings, as well as creative hobbies and recreational activities. The variety of art disciplines which might be part of a creative arts program depends on the strengths and resources of the caregivers and the patient. The most important objective of an arts program is to diminish the impact of crisis created by terminal illness and to improve one's quality of life while at the same time lowering pain levels.

If you are interested in pursuing these various avenues, check your phone book or ask your health care advisors to find out what is available in your area.

Medication

In a hospital setting, medications will be distributed and monitored routinely by the staff. A recent study reported in the *Journal of the American Medical Association* and quoted in *Parents* magazine[6] stated that physicians in a large teaching hospital were found to make, on average, two and a half errors every day in prescribing medication. Half of these errors were health-threatening to patients.

Therefore, let me suggest that you ask nurses questions about medication before taking it. If the medication does not seem to be working or agreeing with you, let them know.

When you are given a new prescription, ask the following questions before having it filled:

What is the name of the medication?
How does it work?

What form (capsule, liquid) and strength is it?
How often should it be taken?
When should it be taken (with meals, before meals)?
How long should it take to see results?
What are the possible side effects?

When taking medication at home, follow the same precautions. If your physician has not answered the questions to your satisfaction, ask the pharmacist so that you can be fully informed before you begin taking the medication. Prescriptions are often very expensive and because I am a drug-sensitive person, I usually fill only half a prescription on a new drug to see how it agrees with me before getting the entire amount. Pharmacists have no problem doing this.

With most pain medication it is important to keep a constant level in your body for it to be effective. Do not skip a dosage because you are feeling better. By skipping doses the level becomes uneven and if you wait until you are experiencing pain it will take added time to get the right level into your system and gain results.

Never mix medication from different pharmacies or doctors without checking with a medical person beforehand. If medication should be taken on a full or empty stomach try to adhere to those rules. If you are unable to eat, and directions state to take it following a meal, take it with a cracker or glass of milk. Read all information that comes with a new prescription and heed all warnings.

Doctors assume a prescription is doing its job unless you tell them otherwise. If you experience unpleasant side effects, notify your doctor. He has no other way of knowing. If the medicine is ineffective, your condition worsens after you have started the medication, or you build up a resistance to it, let your doctor know. Everybody is different and medicines can have unusual effects. It does nobody any good if you suffer in silence. Express yourself so that the best results can be obtained from the many drugs available.

Home Remedies

In addition to prescription drugs, there are many good home remedies. Most families have special little tricks that have been passed down from generation to generation that bring comfort. A cup of herbal tea to calm a person down, an ice pack on a throbbing head, or a good gospel tape for distraction from pain can be successful "medicines." Make use of them.

A hot water bottle can soothe achy muscles or cramps, as can a heating pad. When I'm looking for a home remedy I think back to the ways my mother had for making me feel better when I was a child. In the 1950s we didn't have many drugs available so mothers developed their own methods of treating ailments. My mother used to give me a spoonful of honey for a sore throat and chicken soup with homemade noodles for a head cold. She would also tuck me into bed with one of my dad's giant white linen handkerchiefs under my pillow. It was comforting psychologically and I got well quickly. Today when I get a cold I stuff myself with cold remedy tablets and never pause in my hectic daily activities. It takes me twice as long to get well and is not half as nice as being pampered.

Comfort is the key word here. When we are sick we need to be comforted. Even your caregiver is comforted when he knows he has made you feel better. Do not be afraid to ask for a heating pad or a back rub. Human contact is soothing for both the caregiver and the patient.

A back rub can be relaxing and bring about sleep more easily and it can ease aches and pains. It is also a good preventative of bedsores because it improves the circulation. I like to warm lotion before applying it for a back rub. It makes my hands feel good and is not such a shock to the patient when it is applied. To do this I either place the lotion container in hot water for a short time or warm it on the stove by placing the container in water in a saucepan over low heat. Be extra cautious with plastic containers because they can melt. Also, be sure you test the lotion on yourself before pouring it onto the patient.

Cancer

Many patients with a terminal illness have cancer. Not because cancer is the number one cause of death (it actually ranks second to heart disease), but, unlike heart disease, it usually gives a warning. Many of us know people who have died of cancer and we fear getting it. The actual statistics issued for the year 1990 show there were over six million Americans alive who have a history of cancer, three million of them diagnosed five or more years ago. Although about 76 million people alive today will get cancer, only one in five deaths in the United States is from cancer.

Another mistaken fact about cancer is that it causes painful, agonizing deaths. Even cancer in advanced stages often has little or no pain involved with it. Statistics show that fifty percent of terminal cancer patients experience relatively little pain. Those who do have pain can have it well-controlled throughout the illness. My own father died of prostate cancer that had spread throughout his body. He never took anything stronger than over-the-counter acetaminophen tablets and was quite comfortable.

Both the American Cancer Society and The National Cancer Institute have a wealth of information available and are plugged in to numerous other resources in most communities. If possible visit your local office or telephone them and ask for printed material applicable to your specific form of cancer. If you are interested in being a part of an experimental program when all other treatment has proven ineffective, contact the Physician Data Query (PDQ) for a computer printout of the latest programs being offered in the United States (more information in the back of this book).

The American Cancer Society also has equipment available on loan to qualifying patients. Each local office is different, but it is well worth a visit or telephone call. Inquire about volunteers, support groups, transportation to doctors' appointments, and printed material.

Our local office has all of the above available plus medical supplies that have been donated. In addition, we have a wide range of wigs and cosmetic items to give patients a lift. All these products are given free of charge.

Next, go to the library and check out any materials pertaining to your illness and health situation. Ask around in your community for recommendations, check with medical personnel, talk to people until you feel comfortable with the facts and are confident that everything possible is being done.

AIDS

Although AIDS (Acquired Immune Deficiency Syndrome) is presently without a cure, back in 1982 the life expectancy after diagnosis was an average of eight months. Now it is much longer. Between research and knowledge, the life expectancy could be increased with each passing year. It is important to keep the patient alive as long as possible with such a new disease in case of a treatment breakthrough. Each month, hopefully, brings us closer to a cure.

People do not die of AIDS. AIDS is a virus that destroys the immune system which allows other diseases to take over the body. However, symptoms can be controlled, if not cured, and comfort measures can be used to keep the patient as symptom- and pain-free as possible.

> Anxiety and depression are most common in AIDS patients. Distress similar to patients with cancer and often-fatal diseases is evident in the preoccupation with illness and imminent death. The stress response at the time of diagnosis may be marked by disbelief, numbness, and an inability to face facts.[7]

Only two percent of AIDS patients spend their last days in hospitals. Most are cared for in private homes, hospice units, or special AIDS hospitals. As more knowledge is gained and dispensed, the fear that originally surrounded AIDS victims continues to lessen. Support groups are cropping up so that AIDS patients do not have to die alone without assistance.

Just as with cancer, it is best to be well-informed. Read up on the disease, find available resources in your community, look for a support group. Call accessible "800" numbers to find out where you can get the most help. AIDS hospice units are cropping up all over the country and it is important to research your choices before you become too sick to do so.

Unlike cancer, AIDS is a disease that arrives with much misinformation about its contagion, contraction, and cure. Family support is often withheld, and patients are ashamed to even say the word "AIDS." Consequently, many AIDS patients die without the care that cancer patients receive. It is bad enough to have a terminal disease, one with no known cure, without having people shun you because they feel the disease came about from an unfavorable lifestyle of homosexuality or drug addiction.

If you are an AIDS patient, do not feel compelled to explain the way you contracted the disease. Instead, let people know what is being done to slow down its progress and what can be done in comfort measures at the present time. Try to mend any broken family ties while you have the energy to do so. If you are unable to do this in person, try doing it through letters. This is not the time to be holding grudges or allowing loved ones to be doing likewise.

Hospital versus Home Care

It is vitally important for a patient to be comfortable with his or her own care. Before making any decisions, check all the choices available in your area. Gather available resource materials, be aware of cost structures and maximum health insurance benefits. Find out about possible time limits on benefits and what is available in home nursing care and with volunteer organizations. After gathering all the necessary information, think about the options, then call together all the people who will be affected by your decisions.

Institutional care versus home care is simply a matter of personal choice. However, it is necessary for the patient and his family to be in agreement about it. I have seen patients who wished to remain at home when other family members were reluctant; this caused great friction in the household. When reaching a decision, everyone involved needs to be honest about their concerns and fears. Sometimes simply talking matters out results in resolved differences.

If you feel you would be more comfortable in a hospital setting, being cared for by professionals, than in your own home having loved ones feed and possibly diaper you, it is important to say so. If you have trouble communicating your needs, you may be more comfortable in a hospital setting, being cared for by professionals. If your illness is one that requires care only a professional can administer adequately, skilled hospital care will be necessary and the choices will be more limited.

It is important that everyone is comfortable with the decisions. Talk over everything carefully before reaching any decisions. Then realize that no decision has to be final. Any time a home hospice patient or his family decides professional care would be preferred, they can change their minds and the patient can be hospitalized or placed in a hospice facility or nursing home. A hospital patient who decides he would rather be at home in his own surroundings can ask to be discharged at any time and taken home by ambulance, if necessary. An exception to this is with Medicare-certified hospice care where the rules differ. Before being admitted to the certified program you will be informed of the restrictions.

Hospital Care

Acute care hospitals are now required to discharge patients that do not require skilled care. When this occurs, if it is not possible for the patient to be cared for at home, the remaining options are either a nursing home, convalescent hospital, or hospice care unit. The cost for these facilities is considerably higher than home care with a personal caregiver. Check insurance and Medicare benefits so that all the facts can be carefully weighed. Nursing care that is appropriate in the beginning of an illness may not be suitable months later. There are no certainties with a terminal illness and you must be willing to bend and change with the current circumstances.

A great advantage to both hospital care and convalescent care is that the family does not have to make as many major decisions in regard to personal care. The patient is cared for routinely by professionals, emergencies are dealt with as they arise, and doctor's visits are more frequent. All this frees up other family members so they can go about their daily obligations. Often the person most likely to be the primary caregiver is also the main breadwinner in the family, making it impossible for him to stay home and care for the patient. Unless funds are available for private home nursing care, which can get very expensive, there is little choice other than institutional or convalescent care.

Professional care can be quite satisfactory. I have seen terminal patients treated with great dignity when in the hospital. Often rules are relaxed and every consideration possible is taken to accommodate the terminal patient and his loved ones. They are given a private room when available and placed at the end of the hall so family members can come and go at all hours without disturbing anyone else. I have personally seen various hospital staffs look the other way when loved ones wanted to spend the night or visit during off hours.

One distinct disadvantage for patients in hospitals is that it is more difficult to screen visitors. It is not always possible for the family to spend private time with their loved one. The nursing staff has duties to perform and they cannot accommodate the patient's needs the same way they can be met at home.

For instance, one day I was trying to have a serious spiritual conversation with a very ill friend while the janitor mopped the floor and whistled a happy tune. It was distracting and I finally had to give up in despair. Likewise, there may be times when the patient does not feel like visiting and there is no good way to keep people out of a hospital room. One time I did see a "Do not disturb" sign on a closed door, but nobody was paying much attention to it.

Depending on the situation, pain control may be better or worse in a hospital setting. If the staff is overworked or short-handed, medication may not be distributed on time. However, if shots or IV's are required, the staff is better equipped to handle it. Oxygen is always available and professional consultations ease the burden of the family trying to make decisions.

It also seems easier to maintain cleanliness in a hospital where the professionals know just how to change a bed with a patient in it and give thorough sponge baths. Bedsores are more easily prevented due to general know-how. In the hospital, a pressure sore can be treated immediately, before it becomes unmanageable.

Hospice care units are excellent choices for people who prefer the hospice philosophy but have no full-time caregiver to administer at-home hospice care. To find a hospice unit check in the telephone book or with your local hospital. If you are being cared for by a Health Maintenance Organization (HMO), they will be able to supply you with the information. Another source of information is through the "800" number for your particular illness. For instance, special AIDS hospices are opening all the time in different parts of the country. The AIDS National Hotline would have this information.

Home Care

For the patient to remain at home for the duration of the illness there should be a willing person who will be able to devote twenty-four hours a day to caring for the patient. This person becomes the primary caregiver. In situations where there is no primary caregiver available, the job may be shared, done in shifts, or provided by hired help.

If it is your choice to be at home let this be known. Check into your health insurance benefits and see what is available in home care; ask your family and friends if they would be willing to work out a schedule so that you can keep hired help to a minimum. Again, you can always change your mind if the time comes when you and your loved ones feel professional care would be better for everyone.

At-home care is easiest if a hospice or home health care agency is involved. They can educate the caregivers in health measures that will make care easier and of better quality. Often health insurance benefits will cover the expense of home nursing visits or hospice. Some life insurance companies are allowing benefits to be paid prior to death so that the money can be used to cover the care during a terminal illness. Some health insurance policies have special provisions for long-term care. All options should be investigated to make sure you are using your insurance coverage to the best advantage.

The most positive reason for a patient being cared for at home is that the atmosphere is more relaxed and casual; rigid schedules need not be followed and the patient can be in familiar surroundings. We all seem to feel better in our own homes. At home, loved ones can be actively involved in the patient's well-being which can be very rewarding.

I have observed many home hospice cases and have been involved in the care of my own loved ones. The period of grieving can be greatly decreased if you have had the pleasure of caring for your loved one. My mother and I received frequent daily rewards while caring for Dad that left us with lasting memories which eased our grief.

If you choose to stay at home, look into equipment that will make you more comfortable and make the job easier for your caregiver. Talk to the people at a hospital equipment supplier and explain your needs. They will probably be listed in the yellow pages of your telephone book under *hospital equipment and supplies, medical equipment, home health services, hospices,* or *health appliances*. Ask if there are items they can recommend for your particular situation.

If and when it becomes too difficult to get into a bathroom, a bedside commode is extremely useful. Also available are bedside tables and trays, walkers, wheelchairs, bedpans, urinals, and equipment for lifting, heisting, or for safety. Bars can be installed near the shower or tub for safety, and the commode can be raised with a donut-shaped seat. Other special devices include shower seats, hospital beds, humidifiers, vaporizers, fans, air flotation pads for mattresses to help prevent bedsores, and special foam "egg crate" mattress pads.

Use your imagination for problems that offer no solutions through the ready-made channels. I have seen home remedies that work wonders, such as homemade special-shaped pillows to place at extra-sensitive spots like between the knees or under a sore arm. I have seen a toilet seat wrapped with foam to protect a sore tailbone. I have seen pieces of fake fur wrapped around limbs and beds filled with pillows for propping in a comfortable position. All you need is a little imagination and great things can be accomplished. Do not assume a solution is impossible until you have exhausted every possible source.

Friends love to be called on for suggestions in working out an innovative solution. Don't be embarrassed to call on them with a tricky problem.

Hospice

The word "hospice" is derived from the Latin root word *hospes* which means "the mutual caring of people for each other." The modern words "hostel," "hospital," and "hospitality" were derived from *hospes*. In olden times a hostel was a place where travelers were lodged, cherished, and refreshed. "Hospice" stands for an entire philosophy of life and death where people who are incurably ill can be tenderly cared for as they travel to the end of this life.

Hospice care may be provided in a patient's private home or in a special hospice unit. Either way the hospice philosophy is the same. It is a method of care given in the spirit of quiet and serenity and can be used when a cure is no longer realistic. The hospice theory stresses quality of life rather than quantity, where the main goal is to allow a patient to die with dignity, freedom, and self respect, while at the same time ministering to the family as a group. Indeed, whole books have been written about the art and science of dying naturally, surrounded by loved ones, and the skillful means which allow that process to be experienced more deeply.

The hospice philosophy emphasizes comfort, communication, and peace. The main purpose is to assist the patient in the passage from this life to the next in a natural, peaceful manner, free from pain and stress in a comfortable environment.

In this type of environment the patient and his family feel more in control of the entire situation. To die at home is to die surrounded with love in a familiar setting. Indeed, many of the people who have been taken home to die have found a much diminished need for pain relief because of the relaxed schedule and familiar surroundings.

An important factor in choosing home hospice care is whether there is a hospice organization covering the area where you live or if there is a hospice unit nearby. With a hospice organization the family has great support throughout the illness. Hospice teams assist in the care, but more importantly they educate the family or caregivers in ways to make the job simpler. They can advise on equipment, give baths, change dressings, do professional chores, and offer emotional support. They have a physician on call and a spiritual advisor. Many have a nutritionist and physical therapists on duty.

Hospice organizations usually have volunteers who will act as a family friend and provide respite care, run errands, or just sit and listen as you talk. They often act as the go-between when difficult matters need to be discussed.

It is possible to choose home hospice care without the backing of a hospice organization, but it is not as easy. Books on home care and others that explain the hospice method are listed in For Further Reading.

Resuscitate or No-Code

Once the decision is made as to home care or hospital care, the next matter to be discussed should be resuscitation and/or life support equipment. When everyone is in agreement, the proper papers need to be signed and the doctor needs to be informed and given copies of the paperwork. Every state has its own laws and procedures; find out about your particular area and have everything in proper legal order. For instance, in California living wills do not stand up very well. We have what is called a Durable Power of Attorney. People have found themselves with living wills that were useless when their intent had been very specific. If your will was made in a different state from where you are currently living, make sure everything is in order according to where you are presently residing.

In California, when the paramedics are called out for an emergency they know to check the front of the refrigerator for no-resuscitation orders. If the orders are tucked in a desk drawer the paramedics will be required to administer resuscitation measures even if family members are saying otherwise. Legal issues are sticky. Be very clear on them. Local hospice organizations will be able to advise you. If you have no hospice, check with the county or city offices, the coroner's office, or the fire department about rescue efforts. Pick up your telephone and play detective until you have tracked down someone who can give you the answers you need.

Physical Needs

Your physical well-being involves many areas of need.

Nutrition

Depending on the progression of your illness, your body may no longer require or desire nourishment. When this is the case, it would be foolish to force yourself to eat a certain amount of calories each meal. Liquids are necessary, but food is not. The human body is a remarkable machine; it will let you know what it needs.

If you have no desire for food, it makes no sense to cause yourself undue stress by trying to eat. Often just smelling an orange or eating one bite of a favorite food is all that is required to satisfy you. Go with whatever feels right. Naturally, if you are able to eat, you will feel stronger and more emotionally stable.

I have seen pathetically ill people force down mouthfuls of food, fighting nausea, simply to please their loved ones. Do not get into that cycle; follow your cravings instead. What harm can it do if you have apple pie for breakfast, an orange for lunch, and custard for dinner? If some days your stomach is rebelling against vegetables or meat, it is no big deal. Maybe tomorrow you will crave only a big green salad. If you wish to take in more nutrition, but have no appetite, there are many nutritional drinks on the market. They are similar to milk shakes and are often more appealing than solid food. These drinks come in various flavors and can be purchased in drugstores and most grocery stores. People tell me they also freeze the liquid drinks; this makes them similar to ice cream and more palatable.

It is necessary to get liquids into your body or dehydration will occur. Most people will continue to desire liquids even when they have no appetite for food. As long as you are able to swallow, drink as many liquids as possible. If you find it difficult to drink water, ice chips or frozen juice chips can suffice. Frequent small sips may serve you better than big gulps. Carbonated drinks may cause gas in an empty stomach, as may drinking through a straw. If gas is a problem, switch to fruit drinks instead.

Often cold items are desirable, such as frozen pops, ice cream, and frozen yogurt. Let your tastes be known. Your friends and caregivers are probably waiting with bated breath to serve you some delectable treat. Even if you can only sniff the aroma or eat one bite, it gives those supplying it great pleasure. Do not deny them that personal reward.

Even when you can no longer eat full meals, you can still share in mealtimes. I have seen families take their meals into the room with the patient even when he no longer had an appetite. They could still share in the dinnertime conversation and have a time of fellowship as long as no one was bothered by the fact that the patient was not eating. If the aroma of food does not bother you, reassure your family that you enjoy simply being with them and watching them eat. Possibly toy with a bowl of flavored gelatin just to keep them company or sip your drink along with them. It can be a time of sharing, with nourishment being secondary.

Elimination

When food intake is decreased the bowels will become irregular or sluggish. This is not a major concern unless you are feeling uncomfortable. Lots of people expect to have a daily bowel movement and any change in routine is upsetting. As long as you feel all right, it is nothing to be alarmed about. In case of discomfort or bloating, be sure to let your doctor or nurse know. There are many good remedies on the market that can take care of this situation. Do not self-treat with over-the-counter remedies until you have checked with your health care team.

In case of diarrhea, seek medical care at the onset because it can very rapidly dehydrate someone in an already unstable condition.

When you are no longer able to manage trips to the bathroom by yourself it will be necessary to check into all the other options. Open communication with your caregiver will be necessary. If you want to be helped onto a bedside commode and then left alone until you are finished, say so. Be sure toilet tissue is left within your reach. Ask to have the door closed or a sheet placed over you so that you can be treated with dignity. This is one of the most delicate issues and is difficult for most patients and their families. Open communication makes it less embarrassing. If it is necessary to accept assistance, simply appreciate that it is available, knowing you would do the same for your caregiver if he or she required it.

It sometimes becomes necessary to use disposable undergarments which are similar to disposable diapers. They come in many different sizes and styles and experimentation may be required to find the most suitable one. Loss of bladder control and having to be "diapered" can cause distress for the patient. If this matter is handled gently and openly by both the patient and caregiver the awkwardness need not last for long. The use of disposable undergarments makes cleanliness much easier to maintain and relieves the burden of getting a patient out of bed to a bathroom facility.

Try to overcome any feelings of embarrassment by openly expressing your appreciation for the care you are receiving and not concentrating on the negative aspects of your illness.

Creative Senses

Don't neglect creativity or use of all the senses to bring about comfort. Tap into whatever appeals to you personally. Ask that a tape recorder and your favorite tapes be placed within reach so that if you awaken at night you can play them. If you are having difficulty falling asleep, listen to music while you receive a back rub. A home filled with music will be more relaxing and will seem less like a hospital setting.

When the time comes to be confined to bed make sure it is located in the best place in the house. Do not automatically think you have to be in your bedroom. With home hospice patients, a hospital bed is usually set up in a central location in the house so that the patient can still be a part of the family. Living rooms work well, as do dining rooms or family rooms. Have the bed placed in a light cheerful spot where there is room for chairs around it. You are not trying to be a successful interior decorator at this point. The bed can even be placed in the center of the room. Ask for sheets in your favorite color or design—forget plain white ones. If you have special pictures or knickknacks elsewhere in the house that you want to be able to see, have them moved into your new "bedroom." You might want a television, a vaporizer, or an oscillating fan, depending on what makes you feel more comfortable.

You can wear pajamas or sweatsuits or your favorite jeans. Now is the time to be a nonconformist and think about what makes you feel best. Many male patients grow beards because they dislike being shaved in bed. Find a hairdresser or barber who will come to the house to keep your hair styled. Nothing gives a lift like a fresh haircut. Often beauty schools will allow you to post an ad on the bulletin board asking for someone to come to your home if you do not have a regular hairstylist who will make a house call.

If you are bedbound, be sure you have a means of summoning assistance—a loud bell, a spoon to bang on the bedrail, an intercom, or a whistle to blow.

Do not forget the pleasure of smells. A whole new field is developing in aromatherapy, which involves using odors to relax people. Jonathan Pevsner, a post-doctoral fellow at the Stanford University School of Medicine has done studies on the sense of smell.

> When you smell something it often triggers a memory or an emotion because the sense of smell is most directly connected to the limbic system, where pleasure and emotion and memory are centered. Odorants can have an effect on your mood, perhaps even on your motivation.[8]

Ask for your favorite lotion, after-shave, or perfume. Splash it on after a bath. Ask to have a hanging spice ball or fragrant flowers placed next to your bed. A favorite smell can give both the patient and the caregiver a real lift.

Writing poetry, composing music, doing embroidery, drawing, or painting pictures are just a few ways to express yourself creatively. If you have any desire for a creative outlet, let your caregiver know so that supplies will be available. Often people can express themselves by means of a creative process when they are unable to express themselves verbally.

When a patient is in his own home he can explore these various outlets and set his own rules and regulations. When at home, the dog can sleep in the hospital bed with you as can your spouse. You can stay up all night and catnap during the day. You can get out of bed when you feel up to it or snuggle in with a good book. Experiment and use your imagination. This is your time. There are no ground rules or guidelines. The possibilities are unlimited; the choices, yours.

Sexuality

A person's sexuality does not come to an end with a terminal diagnosis. It is still natural to want to be held and touched and to continue intimate relationships.

If your illness is contagious, be sure you know all the ways in which it can be transmitted and relay those facts to loved ones. If you are not contagious, but have unfamiliar medical equipment hooked up, explain the equipment to others. Remember that a porta-cath may be threatening to someone who has never seen one before. As a knowledgeable patient you can ease fears about loved ones causing you unnecessary pain or dislodging medical equipment by jostling you.

If you are in a hospital bed ask that the sides be let down so that people can get closer to you. Let people know if you want to hold their hand or receive a kiss. Most people will not do these things without an invitation. They worry about invading your privacy and need to know it is all right. If you are unsteady or if there is a danger of your falling out of bed, remind visitors to pull up the sides again before they leave.

Touching is important for both the patient and the visitor. A fond memory that brings a smile to my face is about my aunt as she lay dying. She reached for my hand and I warned her that my hands were unusually cold. As she took my hand she said, "A cold hand is lots better to hold than no hand at all." I let her hold my icy hand for as long as she needed.

Unless there is a risk of infection due to decreased resistance, ask for hugs when you need them! Again, people will often feel hesitant about hurting you or dislodging medical equipment. Hugs are good for both the ailing and their visitors. Put a sign over your bed that says, "I need hugs! Please comply."

Ask visitors to apply lip balm to dry lips, get a fresh pitcher of water, or plump up your pillows. It will make the visitor feel good about helping and will make you more comfortable, too. Do not hesitate to ask. Everyone likes to be useful and they will be grateful to be allowed to fulfill your requests. I always ask what I can do when visiting with someone who is ill. If nothing is needed I feel a bit dejected afterwards. Do not deny people the pleasure of helping you.

Assuming you have addressed the issue of contagion, sexual contact can continue. Communication and honesty are especially necessary in this area. Touching, embracing, and kissing are all joyful experiences that need not be given up when a person is ill. Put your imagination to good use, while using common sense, and let your wishes for physical contact be known. The timing will be vitally important because spontaneous sexual activity will probably no longer be possible. It will be important to plan ahead for private times when you are feeling your most comfortable and when your medication is working most effectively. You will need to be both innovative and creative in receiving and giving whatever sexual pleasures are possible.

In addition to the enjoyment of sexual activity, the release of sexual energy can lessen the stress level and promote more peaceful relationships. If you notice a marked change in your libido, sexual response, or functioning, check with a health care professional. Often illness, treatment, or medication can have a direct effect on these responses. Find someone you feel comfortable discussing personal matters with and do not simply assume you have to set your sex life aside.

Let your loved one know it is still okay to cuddle under the covers and to enjoy each other's bodies. Be open and honest about any feelings of unattractiveness that you may be experiencing due to weight loss, surgery, or treatment effects. We are usually our own worst critics and our loved ones do not even see our defects (thank goodness!). Remind yourself that love has a depth that goes beyond superficial beauty. Think about the way you would feel toward your loved one if the tables were turned.

A little humor goes a long way. Laugh at yourself and try to keep the atmosphere light about physical changes. Set the pace for your loved ones so that you can all be open about the changes while you are reaching a point of accepting them.

When comedienne Gilda Radner was battling ovarian cancer, I was surprised to see so many pictures of her displayed in magazines. Usually people who have been in the public eye are very concerned about appearing at their best physically. Yet, here was Gilda being photographed with very little hair and toothpick thin arms and legs, with dark circles under her eyes, grinning impishly for the camera. I was both touched and impressed by her courage. It was only later when I read an article about Gene Wilder, her husband, that I came to truly understand the situation.

Gene Wilder told *People* magazine that after Gilda completed a series of chemotherapy treatments she lost most of her hair. He said,

> When her hair fell out, she was devastated, but eventually she made jokes about that, too. . . . Those little bean sprouts growing on top of her head were adorable, like a newborn baby. I thought it was sexy.[9]

Being able to call the fine hair on Gilda's head "bean sprouts" made her hair cute rather than distressing. Because Gilda's husband thought she was "sexy" she was able to accept her changed appearance also. A situation like losing her hair could have been devastating to Gilda; instead it was something to joke about because her husband accepted it. Ultimately, when the patient is comfortable with his looks, it frees up others to feel the same way.

In addition to acceptance of your physical appearance, add some romance to your life. The Wilsons are a good example of what a small change in atmosphere can add to the lives of homebound people.

I always looked forward to my visits with Lois and Joe Wilson. When her husband became ill, Lois set up the hospital bed in the family room right next to a large stone fireplace. It was a comfortable setting where Joe could spend his final days. One chilly, rainy day I curiously asked if they ever had a fire in the fireplace. Lois was so caught up in the physical care of Joe that aesthetics never entered her mind. My remark jogged their memories just as I hoped it would and on my next visit

I was pleased to observe a crackling, blazing fire. After looking at the fire, I inquired about Joe's favorite music. They took the hint and the next time I visited there was soft music playing. With a little more prodding I eventually had them spending romantic times in front of a warm fire as they sipped fruit juice and listened to soft music.

These special quiet times can be increased with the gift of free time that prior to your illness may not have been available. Now is the time to live each moment to the fullest.

2

The Emotional Adjustment

In addition to the physical changes that take place with a major illness, there may be a wide array of emotional upheavals.

Emotions in Turmoil

The initial responses of shock and denial are usually followed by anger, depression, yearning, guilt, fear, and/or sadness. These feelings are some of many that can arrive at any time and switch back and forth.

Elisabeth Kübler-Ross was the first person to document the feelings experienced by dying patients. Her research opened many doors on a subject that previously had been kept tightly locked. Dr. Kübler-Ross feels that only when people are able to accept death as a part of life are they able to make the transition peacefully. She also feels that the most precious times in a person's life come only after they realize they are finite.

It is the denial of death that is partially responsible for people living empty, purposeless lives; for

when you live as if you'll live forever, it becomes too easy
to postpone the things you know that you must do.[10]

Scripture says the same thing using different words.
"Teach us to number our days and recognize how few
they are; help us to spend them as we should" (Ps. 90:12
TLB). The King James Version says, "So teach us to number our days, that we may apply our hearts unto wisdom." Tuck this thought in your toolbox and take it out
on bad days to remind yourself that you are preparing
your heart for wisdom.

Anger

Along with shock and denial, and the *Why me?* questions, anger is likely to be on the scene. You may be
angry because you feel powerless and unable to control
the course your life has taken. You may be angry because
it seems as if all your careful plans have fallen apart,
and you are being treated unfairly. Your mind might
feel like a pressure cooker ready to blow its lid.

Some people direct their anger toward their loved ones
or themselves. They may also blame God for this losing
hand he has dealt them. Being angry with God can be
very frightening. I personally feel God understands when
people become angry with him. Their pain must pierce
his heart just as it would any loving father's. He aches
to comfort his children, but as long as anger is surrounding them, he cannot.

If you are experiencing anger, try to visibly remove
it. Find constructive ways to work out your anger so
that it will not erupt unexpectedly and harmfully. I
know a child, wise beyond his years, who told me that
because our heads are round, anger just swims around
inside and cannot get out. He had come up with a solu-

tion for getting anger out of his head. His theory was that there were two methods, one was by mouth, done by talking about his angry feelings and the other was by hand, through writing. Talking about or writing down anger are excellent ways to work it out. This young man's mother got him a tape recorder so he could express his anger on the tapes. It is a good device to use and helped him tremendously.

Another constructive way to vent rage is to find a trusted friend, a support group, a pastor, or a counselor, and talk with them about your angry feelings. As you express your anger, it will slowly ease itself out of your life. If you simply ignore it or repress the feelings, they may spew forth in hurtful and damaging ways or at inappropriate people.

It can be very helpful to write about your anger in a notebook. No one needs to see what you have written. The important part is to put it down on paper and vent it out of your system. Write fast and furiously until you are feeling calmer.

If you are able to participate in physical activities, work angry feelings out with exercise. Pound a pillow or hit a tennis ball against a wall. Go for a brisk walk or sing a lively song with the volume turned all the way up. Do anything you can to release your anger—do not simply let it seethe and simmer inside you.

Depression

Emotional depression is probably the most common symptom in our country today. The number of cases of depression has risen to the level of a national epidemic. One out of every eight Americans can expect to require treatment for depression at some time during his or her lifetime. In any one year it is estimated that between 4 and 8 million people are depressed to the extent that they cannot effectively function at their jobs or must seek some kind of treatment.[11]

If depression is so prevalent in healthy people, is it any wonder that it plays such a huge role in the emotions of a person already weakened by illness? A very normal reaction to a life-threatening illness is depression. Sadness over missed opportunities is natural. The first important step is to identify the feelings of depression. Until it has an identity it cannot be addressed. After the depressed state is recognized, then steps can be taken to deal with it. Left unacknowledged, it will only grow to immense proportions and take over your life.

Shedding tears is not to be confused with depression. Crying is often a way of relieving depression and of expressing oneself in a way that words cannot. Do not be ashamed or embarrassed when you cry. When tears are released they lower the body's stress level and have a relaxing effect on the psyche. If your crying makes your loved ones uncomfortable, be sure to explain where the tears are coming from. Children, especially, feel they are to blame when adults cry. Reassure them that your tears are over the situation and not the result of anything they did.

When you allow your tears to flow you are giving permission to others to comfort you. In comforting you, they are also receiving comfort. To cry alone is still refreshing, but it denies the added solace administered from one human being to another.

Of course, if sobbing becomes uncontrollable or depression is so overwhelming that suicidal thoughts are frequently occurring, then professional help must be arranged.

Depression can be the result of the disease itself or a side effect of treatment or medication. If you are overwhelmed with despair, talk it over with your health care team to see if it is physiological. If so, deal with it from that standpoint. If not, use the same methods of ridding it from your body as you would anger. Talk or write about it. Do not ignore depression, thinking it will go away on its own.

Often depression is the result of anger that has not been worked out and is left to eat away inside. If you do not already have a strong support system, search for one in the form of friends, family, or a support group. Find an unbiased listener who will let you voice your feelings, talk about your sadness, and admit to your despair. Once you have organized your thoughts and identified the reason for your sadness, do not dwell on the negative aspects; simply state the facts and while listening to yourself, be listening for ways to improve the way you feel about your life. For example, make a list of what you are still capable of doing rather than what you can no longer do.

I have observed that perfectionists and depression are Siamese twins—extremely difficult to separate. Perfectionists do constant battle with depression because they can never live up to their own expectations. When a perfectionist becomes ill, it is double trouble. This body that they expected to function perfectly has now let them down. Not only is the body imperfect, but now the person can no longer perform as he wishes. Perfectionists need to accept that humans, themselves included, are imperfect beings. If God is willing to love you in your imperfect state, then you need to love yourself that way also. Life will hold no quality until this is accomplished.

Much of depression can be alleviated by ridding ourselves of the weight of the burdens that we are carrying. Watch the way you sit and stand, or if your shoulders droop down in a defeated attitude. Strive to improve your physical demeanor. When you square up your shoulders and lift your chin it will make you feel better about yourself. Pretend you feel great for a few minutes at a time and pretty soon you will begin to believe it.

Try to treat yourself gently when you are despondent. It is not selfish to be good to yourself. It will help your mental attitude and can often have a positive effect on alleviating physical symptoms. It is all right to pamper yourself with sweet smelling perfume, a bouquet of flowers, or a new pair of pajamas. Even if you are confined to your home or bed you can still find ways to indulge yourself. Friends will probably be eager to help you. Splurge on that book you've been wanting to read or a yummy dessert. After you have babied yourself a bit, it's time to lower your expectations and listen to your self-talk.

Self-talk

We believe most of what we hear. Many of our mistaken ideas come from false self-talk. For the next few days, make an effort to listen to what you are saying to yourself, paying special attention to negative thoughts. Then make a concentrated effort to rid yourself of degrading, negative, melancholy statements. Turn these statements around and speak kindly to yourself. Begin early in the morning to tell yourself you are going to have a good day. Look in the mirror and announce that you are feeling better whether you are or not. Smile and say that you are still a worthy individual even if you are not as productive as you used to be. Talk to yourself as you would a well-loved friend, not an enemy.

When I pay close attention to my own self-talk I notice that I say things to myself that I would never think of saying to another human being. My favorite derogatory statement is to tell myself I'm stupid. I would never call anyone else stupid, but I do it repeatedly to myself in my internal dialogue. Why are we so hard on ourselves?

As you listen to your own self-talk, you can begin to change it so that it will no longer be damaging to your ego. Persons suffering from poor health need a generous amount of caring. Start by giving it to yourself. When you feel better about yourself, you will automatically treat others nicer too.

Yearning

Along with negative self-talk, a feeling of yearning often goes along with depression. With any life-threatening illness comes a natural feeling of yearning; a yearning for time that was wasted, for good health that was not appreciated, for all the things left undone that may no longer be possible to do. Or you may yearn for the plans you had for the future which may no longer be feasible.

Following a terminal diagnosis there will be a change in priorities in your life and possibly role changes. Some plans will have to be postponed, some changed, and some canceled in their entirety. To yearn for unfulfilled dreams is natural, but it can also waste valuable time.

I observed just this in a patient named Alice. Alice had raised a large family, all the time putting aside her desire to write a novel. At last her youngest child left for college and Alice began to place on paper the words that had been forming in her head for years. She had completed the first two chapters when she became ill. She spent the next four months recovering from surgery which was followed up with radiation treatments, all the time hoping to stall the progress of the disease long enough so she could regain her strength and finish her book.

I met her following her radiation treatments. Alice was not only in a deep depression, she was also filled with bitterness and rage. You could feel the despair when you entered her home. Her children eventually stopped coming around, the neighbors stopped visiting, and her husband spent most of his time outdoors working in the yard. Alice talked of nothing but her unfinished book, yet she was never able to get back to her typewriter. She died alone in her room, isolated by disappointment and shattered dreams. Her obsession over her thwarted goal took precedence over a home filled with love and laughter. If she had accepted her fate and simply enjoyed the love of friends and family instead of hanging on to her unrealized dream, her life would have been totally different. Was the price she had to pay worth it?

Each of us sets the scene around us. Have you set the scene in a way to encourage and inspire friendship and love, or in a way that is driving people away? What are you yearning for? Have you arranged an appropriate environment for it? Spend some time in thought to determine your immediate goals. If it is easier to clarify your thoughts on paper, write them down as you reach decisions.

When you set realistic goals and share them with your loved ones you are decorating your life so the curtain of sadness will open and the sunshine can begin to trickle in.

A good way to relieve yearning is by living one day at a time, not looking too far back or too far into the future. Imitate the way children live. They live in the present. They do not fret about the past and they do not put all their hopes in the future. It is a good way to live, for there is no certainty except the present. Make the most of today and do not waste precious moments desiring what cannot be. It is a good idea to talk to your loved ones about your feelings and try not to spend too much time alone when you are depressed.

Guilt

Guilt is easy to recognize because it starts with the phrases, *If only, I should have,* and *Why didn't I?* Guilt is perfectly natural and understandable, but it wastes valuable time and energy when both may be in short supply. Listen for statements that begin with these three phrases and stop yourself and take the time to rephrase them. Turn them into positive statements that will encourage rather than discourage you.

I recently visited a couple who had every reason to feel guilty. Their lifestyle had been less than healthy and now at barely forty years of age, the husband was in the final stages of lung cancer. Ben had been a heavy smoker for most of his life and had abused his body with drugs, poor nutrition, and a lack of exercise.

I glanced at Ben's chart before leaving the office and saw that the cancerous tumor in his body had wrapped itself around his spine; during surgery his spinal cord had been cut so he was paralyzed from the waist down. His situation looked so overwhelming on paper that it was with a heavy heart that I approached his home.

The door was answered by a radiant young woman who was *very* pregnant. I assumed it was Ben's daughter. Instead, Sally turned out to be Ben's wife; she was expecting their first child.

I was pleasantly surprised when I met Ben, too. His eyes sparkled in spite of his weakened condition. Sally climbed awkwardly onto the hospital bed to be close to Ben as we talked. I was instantly warmed by the love, joy, and kindness of this remarkable couple. After we got better acquainted I couldn't help but ask how they had overcome all the negative aspects of Ben's condition.

"Heck," Ben said, in his heavy Southern accent, "who has time to be complaining? I know the odds are against me right now, but Sally and I don't have any time to waste."

I went home smiling, feeling as if I had seen a real-life miracle. Lung cancer in smokers usually brings about a great amount of guilt. It takes a special kind of person to accept what *is* and not wallow in guilt. The past cannot be changed, neither can the future. We have only the present moment to live to the fullest.

If you are being attacked by guilty feelings, release them. Write them down on paper, then tear the paper to shreds or burn it as a symbol of riddance. Or talk about your guilty feelings with a person you trust and get rid of them that way. It is important not to harbor and nourish guilt. Guilt is an enemy, not a friend.

One of my patients told me, "Guilt may visit you, but you don't have to make it a welcome guest." Send guilt on its way by opening the door and saying, "Farewell."

Fear

One woman told me that following her terminal diagnosis she felt a dark cloak of fear covering her that almost suffocated her. It was fear of the process of dying rather than death—a fear of the unknown. Fears multiply in the dark crevices of the mind. When you are able to express your fears, do so. Get them out into the sunshine before they can reproduce and contaminate your life. Ask your health care team for details on your particular illness. Find out what can be done to make your remaining time as good as possible.

Death is an unknown entity. We only die once and nobody can tell us what it is like. Doing anything for the first time is, naturally, frightening. Having to do it with nobody to tell us exactly what it is like makes it even more so. When I was expecting my first baby, I wanted and needed to hear every woman's story about childbirth. It was reassuring for me to know what they had experienced. However, when my time came, my experience was nothing like any I had heard. It was a unique experience, like nobody else's. I believe death will be the same way.

To ease your fears, get medical facts, settle financial matters, and mend broken relationships so that you do not leave any loose ends hanging. The better informed you are, the less insecure and fearful you will be.

An AIDS patient once told Dr. Kübler-Ross that he felt more prepared for death than for the dying process. He believed death would be similar to the relocating he had done many times in his life as he moved about the country with his job.

> So I may be more prepared (for death) than others because I've moved from city to city, leaving those I loved and familiar surroundings behind, and that's what is occurring now. . . . There seems like there's so much to do to prepare for this move and I don't know where to begin.[12]

The process of dying holds no certainties. This young man hated losing control physically and having to depend on others for his care. The loss of his independence frightened him. He did not want to become a burden and had no guarantees that he would not be one before his death.

He talked extensively about "cleaning house." He was cleaning both his physical house and his emotional one, straightening out matters and putting everything in order. He did not want to leave any unfinished business.

Research shows that successful ways to clean your emotional house are by writing and talking. They are the two best antidotes to leaving "your house in disarray." If you do not feel comfortable discussing soul-wrenching feelings, write them down. When you see your fears written on a piece of paper in bold letters, they will not appear as insurmountable.

I have been with many terminally ill people when they died. Not one of these people struggled against death or fought it. They willingly moved out of their bodies, making a smooth transition and leaving a feeling of peace, with a touch of joy, in the room behind them. It was obvious to me that only the body had died, not the person.

Our present bodies are the only ones we have ever had, which causes us to be very attached to them. I have noticed that as death approaches, people seem to become aware that the present body is weak and prone to disease, aches, and pains. They become less enchanted with it. They seem to realize that the body is not really *who* they are, but instead, the dwelling place where they are living temporarily. Letting go of our imperfect bodies will free us to be ready for a better place where we can reside forever.

When I look at a fuzzy caterpillar I have to smile at God's ingenuity. I feel certain that one of the reasons God made those small creatures was so writers would have an analogy to use about life, death, our present bodies, and our eternal bodies. The comparison may be overused and overworked, but it remains the clearest way to explain death and eternal life.

A caterpillar begins its life contentedly crawling about. Then one day it has to give up its peaceful life, the only life it has ever known. It has to give up the furry little body it was perfectly content with up to this point. It does so effortlessly and without a struggle.

Each spring when my children were little, we would capture a caterpillar and watch the process. We would put the caterpillar in an empty jar and watch as it attached itself to the lid and became immobile. Within a couple of days the process was complete. The caterpillar would no longer be visible. Instead, all that remained, attached to the lid of the jar, was a dried, dead-looking shell. But, alas, pretty soon the shell would move. We would then remove the lid from the jar and place it outside so that when the process was complete the beautiful butterfly could fly away.

As the butterfly fought its way out of the cocoon, there would be a lot of flapping of wings while it struggled to free itself. I was told never to try to help the butterfly by freeing it. The struggle it was going through was necessary to dry its wings and strengthen them. To help it would be to interrupt the process and cause it to be unable to fly. The struggle was necessary.

Soon the butterfly would be free and we would watch as it took off, reaching heights that were never before possible to the caterpillar. A butterfly can reach the top of a tree effortlessly and quickly; it can catch a wind current and drift about weightlessly. This new, improved body is not only much more useful, it is also exquisitely beautiful. How can a fuzzy, brown creature turn into an orange, yellow, and black mosaic design? Only God knows the answer. Only God can make a butterfly, just as only God can understand the creature we will become after our metamorphosis.

Try to think of death as the freeing of yourself to become more beautiful. If God cared enough to do all that for a lowly caterpillar, how much more will he do for you?

If your fears seem to be centered on life after death, rather than the process of dying or of leaving loved ones behind, consult a pastor or a trusted friend who is more spiritually mature than you are. Express these fears and seek help in finding answers to your specific questions on eternal life.

One Day at a Time

The time remaining may be mere weeks, it may be months, or it may turn into years. Nobody knows but God; therefore, it makes the most sense to allow God to take over. Pray honestly to accept his will in your remaining days. Live each day, actually each moment, to the fullest without worrying about tomorrow. At this point in life it is important to put the emphasis on quality rather than quantity. Begin and end each day in prayer, either alone or with loved ones. Spending quiet time in thought increases wisdom. Allow yourself the gift of solitude and reflection.

Next, do whatever you feel up to doing on each particular day. Do not force yourself to accomplish great feats, but by the same token do not coddle yourself. Make written lists, if necessary, to set priorities so you will not waste any special moments. Allow yourself to enjoy the feel of warm sunshine on your face or the smell of a freshly opened rose. Make the effort to write letters to distant friends. Do not fall into the "terminal illness mentality" that robs people of quality time.

Deborah Duda in her book, *Coming Home*, writes,

> When we can no longer control the circumstances of our lives, we can still choose our attitude toward the circumstances. We can do this with dying. We can choose to see dying as a tragedy, teacher, adventure, or simply as an experience to be lived. Our attitude will determine the nature of our experience.[13]

One warm summer day, I visited a patient in his home. As I stood next to his bed I looked up and could see into the backyard where the sunlight was reflecting off a gleaming swimming pool. Surrounding the pool were spectacular rosebushes of every shade and color. Yet here lay this man in bed in a darkened room.

I looked at his wife and had a sudden inspiration. "Is it possible for you to help Frank into a wheelchair?"

"Oh, certainly," she answered. "He can get in and out almost by himself as long as I stand close by to steady him."

"How about taking him out to sit by the pool on nice days?" I inquired.

Both Frank and his wife looked at me as if I had just arrived from outer space. "But Frank is very ill," his wife said.

I took a deep breath and looked Frank in the eyes. "Wouldn't you like to sit outside?" I asked, not worrying about trying to be tactful.

The couple exchanged looks and burst into smiles. "I guess we never thought about it," they admitted.

It is common for people to do nothing while they wait to get well or to at least feel better. All past illnesses in our lives have been that way. With a terminal diagnosis the rules of the game change. It is a time of no longer waiting, but a time where immediate action is necessary. What difference does it make if a terminally ill person sits by the pool instead of in his bed? What difference does it make if he is exhausted after going out for dinner at his favorite restaurant? What difference do any of the silly little everyday things we usually worry about make now when life is so precious?

I would like to suggest that you do *whatever* you are able to do, *whenever* you are able. Let your body be your guide. Check with your health care team when in doubt, but use common sense and enjoy each moment. I am not suggesting you take foolish risks, skip medication that is being given for comfort measures, or defy your doctor's orders. I merely want you to think about your choices and how best to enjoy every day to the fullest.

Hospice patients are generally bedbound or homebound, but not always. Some insurance companies require being bedbound and the Medicare-certified program requires confinement to the home except for medical appointments. Nevertheless, we once had a feisty lady in her seventies who had been on hospice for several months when she took a turn for the better. At that point she decided to get out of bed and, to everyone's chagrin, she planned to take a cruise.

"I plan to live until I die," she told the hospice staff as she packed her bag and departed. She took legal papers with her that were handed to the captain of the ship in case she died while out at sea and in her suitcase was plenty of medication for any emergency. However, she did not die. She had a lovely time, gained six pounds, and came home with a glowing suntan. She claimed while on the cruise she had often been extremely tired and had been forced to spend several days in bed. But, for the most part, the trip was fabulous. Back at home she showed visitors the slides of her trip and laughed heartily when she described to them her near shipboard romance.

Another family packed up their van with an oxygen tank and medical supplies, and with one change of clothing and their Bibles took off for a weekend retreat in the woods. They sang around the campfire and breathed the pine-scented air in carefree abandon, making memories that could be stored up and looked back on for many years to come.

Other people who are not as strong physically spend their time writing letters to loved ones and having special quiet visits with friends and family. One man set the video camera on a tripod and made a farewell video for his family with a loving message to each member. Let this time be one of personal choice and doing what feels right to you as an individual. This is the time to throw away outdated rules and useless practicalities.

Relationships

An important part of everyday life is relating to those around you.

Children

Illness and death need not be hidden from children. Allowing children to be a part of such processes will give them a solid base from which to face major events in their futures. When we protect youngsters from the reality that life is imperfect, we give them no foundation for handling their own problems.

I believe it helps children to be involved in the care of a critically ill person and does not harm them. When I was eleven years old I watched my grandmother in her final illness. My mother cared for her in our own home and I feel it showed me by example what compassion is all about. I did not find it frightening. My family was open about discussing all that was going on and what to expect in the future.

Even very young children are aware when major changes occur in a household. To think you are hiding anything from them is to kid yourself. It is better to be up-front with them. Explain the details of the disease as honestly as you can in words appropriate to their ages. Children like to know what to expect and deserve the right to be included. Arm your family with books that can be read to children about illness and death (listed in For Further Reading) and books that tell adults how to explain illness and death to children.

Be sure to explain the facts of the particular illness and reassure the children that they will not get sick, too. Children are very egocentric, and think of everything in terms of themselves. They may wonder if they caused the illness or if they are making the person sicker because they are noisy. Be sure they understand that they are in no way responsible for the disease and make yourself available to answer any questions they might have.

The fear of abandonment is very prevalent in children. Be certain they understand they will be taken care of regardless of what happens. Include them in discussions of plans for the future. Often when young children do not understand the changes in their family or in the household, they act out in anger. They may become angry at the loved one who is ill. Do not make them feel guilty over their emotions.

Nevertheless, it is important to continue to discipline children in the same way they have been treated previously. Discipline gives children a sense of security and they will be feeling insecure enough over all the changes without experiencing a breakdown in rules. Bedtimes need to remain constant as do rules about watching television or checking in with adults before going away from home. Whatever rules were practiced previously should continue to be enforced.

When children act up, let them know that you understand they are having a difficult time and keep the channels of communication open. Encourage them to ask questions and express themselves as much as they are able. Usually children understand more than adults realize.

I have found that teenagers differ in their reactions from young children by putting on a false sense of indifference. It may be because teens abhor being different from their peers. To have a terminally ill loved one does not fit into their nicely ordered scheme of being like everyone else. Therefore, they feign nonchalance or act irritated over the inconvenience of the ill family member. Try not to take this indifference personally or to make the teenager feel guilty for not being more compassionate. The combination of the already over-stressed emotional upheavals of puberty and the disruption in a family with a life-threatening illness is a heavy load for a teen to carry. Act accordingly and do not be offended by inappropriate teen behavior. Acting "cool" is a high priority for teens; do not mistake it for a lack of concern or love.

Both children and teens need to know they are still loved and important even if they have had to take a back seat when the normal routine is disturbed. Try not to overload them with responsibilities. Have someone in the household available to encourage them and to attend the special events in their lives. Birthdays, graduations, sporting events, and school activities may still need adult support. Ask a caring relative or friend to stand in for family members who may be occupied elsewhere during this time.

Other Family Members

Family members who do not live under the same roof as the person who is sick are sometimes a problem. They do not share in everyday progress and daily concerns, or receive any rewards from taking care of the patient. They may arrive on a bad day glowing with good health and full of humorous stories that are entirely inappropriate. This type of behavior can cause hard feelings between the patient, the diligent caregiver who is worn to a frazzle, and the unintentionally blasé relative. Keep an open mind and let other family members be your buffer zone if you are unable to deal with certain people or situations. Remind yourself that each moment is now precious and you do not have time for nursing hurts or resentful feelings.

Visiting relatives may exhaust the patient with inappropriately long visits. The primary caregiver will become finely tuned to the needs of the patient and can assist in this situation. Ask your caregiver to intercede and cut visits short for you, or to screen visitors when your energy level is low.

When my dad was ill, I listened with one ear when he had visitors. When I heard him becoming tired, I went into the room to fluff a pillow or offer a sip of water and asked Dad, "Are you getting tired?" The visitors usually took their cue before Dad even responded and would get up to leave. It was a bit sneaky, but it worked!

Phone calls can be screened by other family members also. When energy is at a premium, it is necessary to conserve it for top priority items. Ask others to do the jobs you cannot handle emotionally or physically.

Friends

Friends can be one of life's biggest blessings. When we are ill they are the bright sunshine following a bleak thunderstorm. Let friends know if you are lonely and let them know when you are not feeling up to company. Invite a friend for a cup of tea if it has been a while since he or she has visited. Often, people are uncomfortable with illness and steer clear of hospitals or sickrooms. You need to let people know that you need them and they need to know they are not intruding but are welcome spots in your day.

Also, when a patient is at home, friends can take a big strain off the caregiver by allowing him or her to take a much-needed afternoon nap or leave the house to run errands. Let friends know when and if you need help. They may simply be waiting to hear from you and will be eager to come to your rescue.

When visiting with friends let them know you are aware of the seriousness of your illness and that they do not need to be embarrassed talking about it. Clearing the air right from the start allows for more honest visits in the future. One especially interesting patient I visited would announce her current medical condition on my arrival. She would recite it like a news bulletin which ended with, "End of medical report. Now let's talk about something interesting!" It was a comical way of setting the stage while letting me know what the status was. She never ceased to amuse me and I noticed she never lacked for visitors.

Unfortunately, certain friends will disappear when illness arrives. This is common and natural. Try not to dwell on these broken relationships. By the same token, unexpected new friendships will bloom at this time and God will send special people to comfort you as long as you keep the doors of your heart unlocked. Accept those who are willing and able to face a critical illness and forgive those who cannot.

Visitors

Any visitor, friend or relative, can be a godsend at times and a problem at others. Concentrate on open communication and try to let your visitors know your current needs. If you are ready to take a nap when someone shows up to visit, you may have to tell them you are not up to visiting. "Would just a quick hug do for today?" you can ask.

Most people visiting an ill person will respect these wishes and be happy about your honesty. Nobody wants to cause undue stress on the patient or caregivers. Often, they merely want to let you know they care; the amount of time they spend with you is secondary.

If you are uncomfortable with telling people you are not up to visiting, put the blame on somebody else.

"My wife says I'm only allowed visitors for fifteen minutes because it wears me out too much," or some such remark should do the trick.

It is not rude or selfish to put your needs first when you are dealing with an illness that is sapping your strength. If you wish to have visitors be a blessing instead of a burden, it will be necessary to use this form of open expression of your wishes whether you are in the hospital or at home.

Communication

Different people will serve different needs in your life and communication will be varied. Regardless of the relationship, honesty is vital. Nobody can ease your mind or be a true friend if you are putting up a false front. Do not say you are "just fine" when you are not.

There are many options. Choose the best ones for each individual and each family member. Begin by opening the lines of communication. Often the patient has to take the initiative in spite of failing health and a low energy level. Statements can begin with the word *if*—"*If* I don't get well, maybe we should talk about our options."

Families accustomed to using humor may introduce the subject of a terminal illness with dry humor, "Don't start counting your inheritance yet, but the doctor doesn't seem to think I'm going to get well. Let's toss this idea around a bit."

Open communication is easier for some people than others. You may have to work into it gradually. In addition to "if" statements make "I" statements. "I really prefer to feed myself." "I'm not up to company right now." Use statements that allow others to know how you are feeling, not wishy-washy questions like, "Do you think I could feed myself?" or "Should we invite Tom over?" Nobody can read your mind and you need to let your feelings be known. "I" statements clear the air and take less energy for everyone.

Often visitors will ask about your health. Try not to spend too much time with medical details. Being part of the normal world is good. Give a brief medical update and then tell your visitor you want to hear about healthy things, similar to the way my special patient did. It will give both of you a boost. Ask friends to bring photographs so you can share events that are important in their lives. It will make you feel more a part of the world outside instead of the constant world of medication and treatments.

While I was helping take care of my father, I had a friend who would call almost every evening. He would ask about my dad and then about my day. There were times when I would tell him I did not want to talk about my day. "How about if you tell me a funny story instead?" I would ask, when I was badly in need of a laugh. His stories took me out of my world for a little while and gave my spirit a genuine lift.

This same friend taught me not to accept "okay" and "just fine" as answers from caregivers when asked how they were doing.

"Yeah, yeah," he'd say to me when I said I was okay. Then he'd counter with, "But, how are you *really*?" It taught me to be more honest in expressing myself and to listen more carefully to others.

My three daughters kept in touch with me by long distance telephone calls, as did my husband. Every morning my dad would ask if I had talked to my family the night before. If I answered with a "no" he would frown. "You must talk to them every day," he would insist, realizing the importance of those times of respite. Since he was paying the phone bill, I assured him I would try to call home more often.

Watch for signs of weariness in your caregivers. Suggest they invite a friend over or leave the house, if you can be left alone. Do not let everyone become consumed by your illness. Suggest playing a game of Monopoly or renting a movie on a videotape. You may have more time for thinking up these ideas than the person or people who are involved in the everyday practical chores.

And most important, communication can be used for more than expressing needs or feelings. Communication can be used to release feelings, give someone a lift, or express appreciation. Communication is more than exchanging words. It is hearing the fear in a person's voice and tuning in to it. It's someone saying, "How are you *really*? Tell me about it." Communication can be the squeeze from hand to hand when no words are appropriate or the acknowledgment of sad news with tear-filled eyes. It's voices mingled in hearty laughter and arms wrapped around each other.

Communication should become a top priority following a terminal diagnosis. Daily routines and relationships change. Priorities need to be discussed so that no valuable time is wasted.

Priorities

In order to feel like you still have some control over the course your life has taken, set priorities. They may be short-term or different ones than before your illness, but you can still be the one to make the decisions.

List your priorities on paper, being realistic. An around-the-world cruise may not be possible, but a trip to the beach with the family may be. Make reasonable plans so you can look forward to them. Have something on your calendar other than doctors' appointments.

Share your list with your loved ones, especially your primary caregiver, so that you can work toward these goals together. Let people know you want to do as much for yourself as possible. Take over any chores that you can handle physically. Maybe it was not your job previously to balance the checkbook, but now you can manage that task easily while handing over your job of cutting the lawn to your spouse. Make whatever changes seem necessary so that life has meaning and each day has a purpose. Let others in on your goals so that they can help make them possible.

Goals

Goals are important to our feeling of well-being. Short-term goals can be just as rewarding as long-term ones. Set some simple goals for each day and some short-term goals for the month ahead. Make the goals reasonable. A goal may be as simple as making a few phone calls to keep in contact with out-of-touch friends or something tangible like a piece of needlework. Goals written down on paper and marked off when completed can add to a feeling of satisfaction and help to get rid of the feeling of uselessness.

An important goal should be to live each day with as much quality as possible. The will to live is very strong. Take advantage of that strength. A strong self will can help to keep hope alive. Continue to be hopeful. A positive attitude and good thoughts about your condition can prove to be helpful. Picture yourself as strong and healthy. Rebuke the enemy forces in the name of Jesus and ask God to destroy the illness in your body and make you whole. Do not claim the illness as your own such as, "*my* lung cancer" or "*my* liver ailment." Do not show any acceptance toward this invasion against your good health. Remind yourself that the words we speak, aloud or in self-talk, can become fact. We want the facts to be realistic, but positive rather than negative. Think of your illness as an enemy and fight it as you would a harmful foe.

Do not use mental imagery exclusively, ignoring the doctor's instructions, but use it in connection with prayer and positive thinking. Like my friend Eula Jean who wanted to cover all the bases, cover all aspects of mental, physical, and emotional healing. It may allow you to cut down on the amount of pain medication you require to stay comfortable while giving you a sense of having some control over your body's condition.

I have been blessed with a wise husband who often straightens out my panicky thinking with a simple statement. It happened again recently. We were six years into a drought in California and it made everyone wary about future water rationing. I talked to my friends about it, frequently wondering what was going to happen to us. Should I plant flowers in my yard or not? I asked my daughters for their opinions. Nobody had any answers. My husband was the only one to suggest I call the privately-owned water company that serviced our small town and ask them what I should do.

I did just that. They apprised me of the current condition and the ways they were working to take care of the summer months to prevent rationing. They could make no guarantees, but I at least had the latest, correct information. When I relayed the information to my husband he smiled smugly and said, "It helps to go directly to the source."

Ah, yes, The Source. When we are troubled or in doubt or need more information, it helps to go directly to The Source. You can do that by talking to your health care team, your loved ones, and, last in this sentence but first on the list, by praying. Take your questions to the Lord in the form of prayer. Ask for answers, for comfort, and for guidance as you face the days ahead. "What do you want me to do with this experience, Lord?" "How can I best put it to use?" "What goals should I have for my remaining time?" Ask in prayer and then listen. Listen to the soft quiet voice that may come in the middle of a still night. Listen to friends who often bring messages directly from God. Listen to loved ones as they express their wishes or their own needs. Listen and set your goals according to those needs.

Loneliness and Isolation

Terminally ill patients tell me that the loneliness they experience after hearing their diagnosis is overwhelming. First of all, they feel nobody understands what they are going through, and second, they feel isolated by their inability to participate fully in activities. Often friends are scared away by illness. They do not know what to say or do so they simply stop coming around. The feeling of abandonment can be very real.

The patient, in addition to coping with devastating news, must now reach out to others and make the first move. If the feeling of loneliness is overwhelming, it might be necessary to seek professional help in the form of a therapist or a support group. Pastors, hospitals, and doctors can often point you in the direction of help. If you are associated with a hospice organization, do not turn down their offer of a volunteer.

I was a volunteer coordinator for hospice for several years and I can vouch for the caring individuals who go into that line of work. They will become a source of great comfort and strength to you and your family, filling the empty places in your lives and your hearts that have been left by friends who were unable to cope.

Hospice volunteers are very comfortable with the subject of illness and death and can offer you a vast array of knowledge from their personal experiences. They are generally available from two to four hours a week for respite care, emotional support, and any varied number of practical tasks. Do not miss this opportunity to make a heartfelt friend.

Now is also a good time to put your imagination to work. Look around and figure out ways to overcome your feeling of isolation. If a simple matter like sharing at mealtime is no longer possible due to a lack of appetite or nausea, you can still find ways for togetherness. Ask the family to eat buffet style once in a while so you can join in the conversation even if you are unable to eat. Let your loved ones know that you are feeling alone. Express your concerns and ask that changes be made in the household so that you can feel as if you are still a part of it.

If you are in an acute care hospital or a hospice unit, ask to have personal articles like pictures or knick-knacks brought and placed about you for a more homey atmosphere. Check with the staff for ways to feel less isolated; inquire about walks on the grounds using a wheelchair or for taking your meals with others. If you are in a room by yourself, find out if another patient is also lonesome and would appreciate a short visit from you periodically.

For the homebound, I have suggested the bed be moved to a central location rather than remain in a bedroom where the patient might feel isolated. If you are uncomfortable with any setup after trying it, gently ask that it be changed. Ask to ride along in the car when errands are being run; a change of scene can do wonders for the disposition! If you are bedbound, invite people to sit on your bed. Often loved ones are isolating you out of concern for your well-being and do not realize that you are feeling left out.

When my aunt became ill and was bedbound, she would bang on her bed when she heard us laughing in the kitchen. "Come laugh in here with me!" she would tell us, as we all moved into her room and shared the joke. Unfortunately, there was no place close to the kitchen for her bed, but she at least let us know her needs.

Another good way to beat feeling lonely is with the use of a telephone. A cordless phone might be purchased or borrowed and placed next to the bed. Patients love to receive phone calls and like the freedom of being able to use the telephone. Ask for a telephone book and your personal address book so everything is within easy reach when you need to talk to someone.

Wheelchairs are also wonderful devices for use against loneliness. They can be used for patients who are unable to walk so they can move about the house and be with everyone else. Wheelchairs can make outings away from the house so much easier and less tiring for both patient and caregiver. There are lightweight models that fold easily for taking in an automobile. A wheelchair can make the difference between sitting in a chair at home and being able to go for a walk in the mall or for a stroll in the park. Anywhere you go you will see people in wheelchairs; it is no longer unusual. Restaurants are set up to accommodate them as are shopping centers and public restrooms. If you expect to be going out often, apply for a handicapped sticker so you can park in designated areas for easy access into buildings.

Role Changes and Values

With illness comes a necessity to change roles. Often the husband finds himself doing the kitchen chores while the wife takes over tasks like balancing the checkbook. The delicate balance and the role changes can make a household feel shaky.

People are usually uncomfortable in new roles that have previously "belonged" to another member of the household. Talk about these feelings and try to divide and delegate tasks in the most practical way possible.

Fortunately, roles are not as carefully defined today as they were twenty years ago. Therefore, role changes are less apt to be disruptive to youngsters or to the adults performing them. Women pump gas, take out the trash, and chop firewood. Men do laundry, cook dinner, and vacuum carpets. When it is necessary to change roles, children often enjoy the variety.

However, remember that children need to remain as children. Remind your family of this. When a father is ill, I have often heard people making the innocent statement to his young son telling him he is now "the man of the house." Children should not have these enormous demands placed on them. They should be assured that the adults will continue to take care of them. They can be asked to do extra chores, within reason, but they should not be made to feel as if they have to become adults overnight and shoulder the whole load.

Try to keep the daily routine as normal as possible, regardless of who plays what roles. When a household is running smoothly it is easier for family members to deal with necessary disruptions. Often it is small inconveniences that wear away a peaceful environment and raise the stress level. Keeping laundry caught up so nobody runs out of socks, having milk in the refrigerator so nobody has to skip their morning cereal, and paying the bills so the phone does not get shut off are all necessary tasks that make bigger problems easier to face. If you have to delegate chores from your bed, do so. Take up those offers of "let me know if I can do anything to help" that frequently come from friends and family.

Children make good helpers and are usually willing to run upstairs for a blanket or to the kitchen for a glass of water. They have more energy and their legs can be put to good use as long as they are not overburdened or have to neglect their own activities.

Be sure your children know you appreciate their extra help and that everything is temporary at this time. Chores may change from day to day and the household situation can be constantly re-evaluated so it can be run efficiently with the least effort.

Children love it when adults stop moving about frantically and give them some eye contact and attention. Do not feel bad if you cannot go outside and toss a ball to your son. He will probably be just as content to have you help him build a model airplane or simply read the instructions to him as he does the work. It is educational for children to be a part of a household that is caring for someone with a catastrophic illness.

Even very young children learn more from watching than from lectures. When children see a family working together and caring for a family member who is ill, they are learning about compassion and love. It is showing them that families stick together through the tough times and that love flows even more freely during those desperate hours.

My babies were all cesarean births. When I came home from the hospital with my third child, my two preschoolers were a great help. I would have them, "Go pat the baby until I can get in there," or reach into a bottom drawer for me to save as much painful movement as possible. They were excited to help with the new baby and we all worked together as a family. Even so, I was quick to reassure them that, "Next week Mommy won't need as much help." In the evening, when Daddy was home, the kids got to be kids again and not Mommy's helpers.

I was careful to make the chores fun. When I needed to rest, we all climbed onto my king-sized bed and the kids read books to me while I rested. I knew they were safe and couldn't get into anything harmful as long as they remained on the bed with me. They loved the extra attention, even though my eyes were shut, as long as I remembered to respond to their questions with an occasional "Uh-huh."

Teenagers, too, learn by observing. They pretend not to notice, but they are carefully watching to see our reactions and they will most often copy those actions when they are adults.

When my father was ill and I was out of town for over a month helping to care for him, I often had pangs of guilt. My youngest daughter was preparing for her high school graduation and my eldest daughter was making arrangements for her wedding. I felt I should be at home to help and support my daughters with these preparations. A wise friend eased my guilt when she told me the example I was setting for my children was more important than being available to them.

"You're showing them that responsible adults take care of their elderly parents when they are needed and that death is a part of life that should be shared, not hidden. They are seeing your priorities and learning a valuable lesson. Ten years from now they won't remember who made the telephone call to order the helium balloons for their party, but they *will* remember that you were at your dad's bedside holding his hand as he lay dying."

Decisions

Among the decisions terminally ill persons must make is one concerning disposal of material goods.

Giving Items Away

My mother has been giving away personal belongings for years. At first it bothered me terribly. "Why are you doing this?" I asked. "You're in perfect health." I did not want to face the fact that the day might come when my mother would no longer be around. But after years of watching her give away her belongings I came to understand and appreciate her philosophy.

At first she laughed and made light of it, brushing it off by saying it would make less for her to dust. But as she got older and the family became accustomed to her dividing up her precious items, we came to see that she took great pleasure in this task. When I was married thirty years ago, she packed boxes of things for me to take, telling me the story behind each of the items. "This is the tablecloth that was purchased for my bridal shower," she said as she packed a large white Battenburg lace tablecloth in a box. "This is Spode china," she told me as she packed the next item. It gave her great pleasure to share with her loved ones instead of waiting for us to inherit her things when she could not see our appreciation or receive the pleasure herself.

When her granddaughters were married, she repeated the process. She took out boxes and filled them. Every time I visit her she says, "What do you want to take home with you?" I am no longer embarrassed over this nor does it depress me. I understand completely. There is a list in her dresser drawer itemizing things which she insists certain people have. The list makes her feel secure and will hopefully keep us from any sibling disputes when Mom is not around to referee.

Part of saying good-bye is parting with material objects. If you feel uncomfortable at this point in your life about giving material items to friends and family, at least make a list stating anything in particular you want someone to have. Is there an item several people will want? Designate who is to have it. I have helped some of my terminal patients label the backs or undersides of items with a person's name so that there will be no question who is to have it.

This is not morbid. It is allowing you to have some control over the disposition of your worldly goods. When you are no longer here, these material goods may give comfort to loved ones. All over my house I have small mementos from loved ones who have died just as I have gifts from loved ones who are still living. I think about these people as I dust each item or water the plants they have given me and it makes me feel closer to them. Sure, I would remember them without the material article, but there is comfort in touching something they once owned and cared enough to leave with me.

Choose the method that makes you most comfortable, either leaving a list, marking items, or making the gift presentation right now. Different people will react differently; some can handle it and some cannot. There are no right or wrong feelings. Often, the disposal of goods will open the door to meaningful dialogues about life and death and have a cleansing effect on everyone.

This is an area where hospice volunteers can be a big help. Ask their advice and possibly have them help with the labeling or disposition of items.

Legal Matters

In addition to the personal closure or saying good-bye and disposing of material goods, it is necessary to have everything in legal order for your peace of mind. These issues will vary from state to state, but I will try to cover all the important aspects so that you will know what must be approached in your particular situation.

Everyone needs a will. People continually tell me that they do not need a will because they live in a community property state, or that they do not have anything to leave anyone. I repeat, *everyone* needs a will, regardless of the situation. It must be current and in writing.

Forms can be purchased from office supply stores; all you have to do is fill in the blanks. When I last checked, they cost under $10.00. In California, it is preferable to use a California Statutory Will. These forms are also available through office supply stores. Likewise, there are currently inexpensive computer programs which can be purchased and done in your own home. You do not need to see a lawyer if you have a simple estate. Just follow the instructions carefully; they are uncomplicated and thorough. Other options are joint tenancy versus community property. It can make a difference in the estate going into probate and also in the way tax bases are figured.

If you need a lawyer and are eligible for senior citizen services, many senior centers, AARP, or other agents or organizations offer free legal services to senior citizens. Making a will does not need to be an ordeal or a financial burden. Be sure it is signed according to the instructions and notarized if necessary. Put it in a safe place and let family members know where it is kept. Have several copies, possibly one in a safe deposit box and one with a trusted family member, one with an attorney, and a copy to each person who is mentioned in the will.

If minor children are involved be sure the guardians have agreed to raise your children and financial arrangements are spelled out.

Another legal document that should be in order is a Durable Power of Attorney or in some states a Living Will. These are instructions for life-sustaining equipment and resuscitation orders when you are unable to let others know your choices. It is very important that these be on proper file and that family members are aware of your wishes.

Do you need a living trust? Do you wish your property to go immediately to your heirs? Should you make provisions now to take advantage of tax breaks? Have you appointed an executor? If a large estate is involved it is imperative to make an appointment with a CPA or an attorney.

It is also helpful to have a trusted second party who is able to sign checks on your accounts. This is called "giving someone the power of attorney" or a "guardianship." There may come a time when someone else needs to pay your bills or withdraw cash from your account. It makes it much easier if a second party is prepared and authorized to do this before the need becomes urgent. Bills continue to arrive regardless of what is going on in a household. When my mother had a heart attack and was hospitalized suddenly, it made life much simpler when my sister could keep up with the mail and pay the bills. Conversely, when my neighbor was suddenly hospitalized, nobody could sign his checks or had a key to his house. By the time he was released from the hospital his utilities had been turned off, and all sorts of messes had to be straightened out at unnecessary expense and great inconvenience.

Another matter that makes things easier for others is to set up a special folder of important documents. The Durable Power of Attorney, resuscitation orders, life insurance policies, legal documents such as your social security card, driver's license, birth certificate, marriage certificate, bank books, military discharge papers, stock certificates or records, real estate holdings, organ donor card and phone numbers of doctors, funeral directors, and any others who need to be notified as to your condition should all be together in a special folder.

It is never too soon to take care of legal matters and it is simple to keep them updated. It will give you peace of mind and save your loved ones undue problems.

Suicide

I recently read that suicide hotlines receive a great percentage of telephone calls from people with terminal illnesses. I decided to check into this and called three suicide hotlines to ask for statistics and was told there were none available. The people I spoke with claimed they had very few calls from terminal patients themselves. However, they did get many phone calls from the caregivers of terminally ill patients who were concerned that their loved ones might be suicidal.

Statistics show that when people are without hope they will consider suicide. I have tried to stress in this book that even when there is nothing more that can be done medically, there is still hope. When a doctor tells a patient that there is nothing more he can do, it means that he has run out of medical treatments or medication which will improve the condition. The various symptoms can still be treated to bring about comfort if not a cure. The body may restore itself to good health or remain uncured without getting any worse for years. Remind yourself that God is always capable of miracles. There is always hope!

People, and Americans especially, equate production with worthiness. The more we do, the better we feel about ourselves. When illness hits and we have to stop producing and take time off to allow our bodies to mend we are devastated. We must remind ourselves that a person is still a worthy human being even when he is nonproductive in the usual sense of the word. We are still who we are, even when we are ill. Our loved ones love us because of *who* we are, not *what* we do. Whether you are winning a marathon race or only holding a hand while sick in bed does not change *who* you are. Concentrate on the meaningful things that remain in your life, such as providing love, encouragement, laughter, and prayers, instead of what is no longer possible.

Suicide should never become an option. If suicidal thoughts come creeping in, they need to be shared with someone who can help you sort them out. Suicide is a tragic end to life. It leaves wounds, often untreatable wounds, to those left behind for the rest of their lives.

I have personally known two terminally ill patients who committed suicide. The aftermath was heartbreaking. The loved ones left behind were almost drowned by waves of guilt that washed over them for many years. They blamed themselves for not seeing it coming and preventing the suicidal act. The suddenness of the death denied them the pleasure of taking care of their loved ones and they were denied any feel-

ing of closure, making the period of grief intense, difficult, and lengthy. One woman was left financially
strapped due to a suicide clause in her husband's life
insurance policy of which he was probably unaware.

The two men who committed suicide were likely
thinking they would save everyone a lot of trouble if
they removed themselves before they became a burden
to others. But instead of their deaths making life easier,
they left a path of destruction behind—destruction that
can never be undone—words left unsaid that can never
be said, and guilt that will nag forever.

Please, please, if you are feeling beyond hope and
thinking you are a burden on your loved ones or are
using up financial resources, discuss the situation with
someone—anyone—a friend, relative, or professional.
Allow them to help you sort out the truth from your
hopeless feelings. Allow God to choose the method and
time when your life will end; do not take it on yourself
to do this. It is the cruelest act you can force on loved
ones and interrupts any plans God has for you.

3

The Spiritual Approach

Randy Becton, who was diagnosed with advanced lymphoma (an aggressive cancer) in 1973 writes:

> My outlook is filled with hope. Tremendous advances have been made through cancer research; methods of treatment and control are constantly being improved. Many of us may successfully battle this disease—and win. Others of us may be able to be long-term survivors. Nevertheless, my deepest hope is not in research or treatment but in God. My security and confidence grow out of my being a Christian. Cancer can't threaten God's plan for his sons and daughters. This knowledge is my source of hope and peace.[14]

Giving God Control

Security is important; it makes us feel safe when we think we are in charge of the course our life is taking. We set goals, make long-range plans, and go about our business, never thinking that we are not in control.

We are reminded that we are not directing our own fate when a dead battery keeps us from attending an appointment, bad weather makes us cancel a picnic, or illness prevents us from fulfilling our plans. When our carefully laid plans are interrupted, reality grabs us and shakes us, making our security fall to the ground in a heap.

In most instances we can remedy the situation by calling a repairman, postponing the picnic until tomorrow, or simply waiting until we get well. Then we smile, raring to go, thinking we have matters under control again. These little changes in plans merely stop us momentarily, but they do not convince us that we are not the ones in charge the same way a critical illness does. With a terminal diagnosis, fixing the battery or simply waiting until next week is not going to do the trick. We must give in to a stronger force and admit that life is out of our hands.

As soon as people, sick or well, begin to let go of their clutching control, life becomes less a struggle and more a pleasant journey. Have you ever had a sock-pull with a puppy? The harder you try to pull the sock away, the tighter the puppy will hang on. As soon as you let go of your end, he usually drops his end, too, perks up his ears, wags his tail, and waits for the battle to begin again.

A life-threatening illness can also become a power struggle. The harder you try to hang on emotionally, the less strength you will have to combat the illness physically. It is important to use your strength wisely. Instead of tugging for control, let go of your end and pray for God's will in your life. It need only be a simple statement such as, "Your will be done, Lord."

If you are unaccustomed to praying this way, it will be difficult at first. You will want to fight back and pray to get well. You will wish to grab back the feeling of control. Nevertheless, repeat the words anyway even if you do not feel sincere. With practice, the words will come more easily and eventually they will come from your heart instead of your mouth. At that time, you will feel the release of a heavy burden and be filled with peace. The torrential winds that have been tossing you about will calm down and you will be able to stand firm and strong. I have a friend who tells people in emotional upheaval, "You can't direct the winds, but you can certainly adjust your sails!" Adjusting your sails allows you to be at peace rather than engaged in a struggle.

Prayer

So many of us pray as a last resort. To leave prayer as a last resort, however, deprives us of our most valuable source of strength and comfort. Often when we are depressed and downhearted, it is difficult to know what to pray for, or even to find the energy to pray. Prayers need not be fancy words or structured exercises. They can be as simple as the single word—Help!

You can explain in your own words that you are discouraged and do not even know how to pray at this time. You may prefer to read comforting Scripture aloud as you prepare your heart and mind for prayer. The Psalms are filled with beautiful phrases of comfort and thanksgiving. I have a difficult time memorizing Scripture verses so I prefer to quietly sing praise choruses for comfort.

Praying can also be done in the form of listening. If we do all the talking, we can miss important messages. Try to spend some wordless, quiet time with the Lord. Inner healing often takes place during times of quiet solitude. It may take time for inner healing, but eventually a glimpse of the completed picture will appear and help to renew your faith.

The Bible tells us, "Don't worry about anything; instead, pray about everything; tell God your needs and don't forget to thank him for his answers. If you do this you will experience God's peace, which is far more wonderful than the human mind can understand. His peace will keep your thoughts and your hearts quiet and at rest as you trust in Christ Jesus" (Phil. 4:6–7).

Also, Scripture assures us that when we don't know what to pray or how to pray, the Holy Spirit will take over and express our needs to God. Romans 8:26 states, "And in the same way—by our faith—the Holy Spirit helps us with our daily problems and in our praying. For we don't even know what we should pray for, nor how to pray as we should; but the Holy Spirit prays for us with such feeling that it cannot be expressed in words."

Trying to Understand Illness

There is no way for us to understand illness. Many things are beyond our understanding—pain, sickness, an untimely death—but even if we do not understand them, we can still be at peace about them. Struggling to find answers to unanswerable questions only wastes time and energy.

Who can comprehend the reason that a young husband, eagerly awaiting the birth of his first child, is struck down by a malignant brain tumor? Or the reason that a teenager is killed by a drunk driver when she is returning home from church? There is no way to understand why a young man who dearly loves his family gets terminal cancer while an abusive alcoholic lives for eighty-two years.

There are no answers to these questions. Friends and family tell us to draw on our faith and trust in God. People in crisis hear many clichés. Often when people do not know what to say they fall back on clichés or platitudes which do not provide much comfort. Instead, they merely make us feel more isolated and misunderstood.

When tragedy hits we do not feel like being strong or having faith, yet that is exactly what the clichés tell us to do. Ordinarily, our faith falters when tragedy hits. We do not want to trust God after he has not prevented us from the pain we are now enduring. We are angry, desperate, and filled with fear. But worst of all, nobody seems to understand. Continue to look for that one special friend who *does* understand. Try to express yourself as much as you are able in the hopes that eventually others will truly hear.

Life may seem useless, but with time the final result will unfold. God has plans that do not always match our own and it can be difficult fitting the pieces of the puzzle together when we do not know what the completed picture will be. This is where faith and trust take over.

I recently read about a young man whose life took a devastating twist, but actually turned out better than he ever imagined. This particular young man grew up knowing he wanted only to be a missionary. He had a burning desire to travel to faraway lands and tell the people about Jesus. He studied his Bible and read books about missionaries just waiting until he could become one. When the time came to leave from New York to go to Africa, he found his wife was too ill to survive in the African jungle. All his dreams of being a missionary were shattered. He had no choice but to take up another career.

His father had been working to produce a non-fermented grape juice that could be used in churches for communion. The young man took over the business and developed the juice. As a result, he became extremely wealthy and was able to donate many millions of dollars to missionary work. He was unable to be a missionary, but instead, he was able to provide extensive help to many nations. Out of his wife's illness came years of missionary activities that would not have been possible had he become a missionary himself. His name was Welch and we still enjoy his grape juice today, many years later.

God had bigger plans for Mr. Welch than to be a missionary. He was not denying this young man's desire out of meanness—he simply had other, greater plans for him. By being obedient and following God's plan, Mr. Welch was able to accomplish an even greater mission in life.

When catastrophic illness arrives it brings with it a whole new set of plans for the entire family. Joni Eareckson Tada, who became a quadriplegic as the result of a diving accident when in her teens says, "You may not be able to know the meaning of every event, but you can know that every event is meaningful." I do not believe it is possible to fully understand life here on earth nor control our futures. Only when we give up trying can we live peacefully.

Making Amends

In addition to giving up the desire to command our own futures, it is necessary to let go of problems from the past. Hanging on to them can disturb the peaceful environment we desire. Broken relationships and hostile feelings will stand in the way of pleasure.

When each moment is valuable, do we want to have a closet filled with bitterness, anger, hate, grudges, fear, and rage, or do we want to fill that space with love, joy, peace, serenity, and tranquility? The decision is ours. Others do not make us feel angry or guilty or bitter. They may do things that cause us to feel a certain way, but they are not responsible for our feelings. Each person is the owner of his particular feelings. Are you possessing feelings you do not really like? Hurtful ones? Destructive ones? Are you harboring ill feelings that do not actually belong to you?

Unforgiveness hurts the person who possesses it, not the recipient. If you have feelings of unforgiveness or are nursing a grudge, it is hurting you by preventing good feelings from surfacing. Unforgiveness also becomes a block in our relationship with God. Negative feelings can take up internal residence and gnaw away inside while it tries to escape. The only way to replace it is to let it all emerge and make a vacancy. Only then can peace and joy, happiness and tranquility replace unforgiveness in your soul.

I have a friend who says, "My feelings belong to me. Why should I let others decide the way I am going to feel?" This friend has a sense of inner balance which is lacking in most of us. He knows what he stands for and who he is. He behaves as he knows he should. He refuses to return hostility for hostility.

He continues to explain that praise does not give him a feeling of false euphoria nor does criticism tear him down. Snubs do not hurt him and he does not become depressed when others treat him unfairly. "To let another person determine whether I shall be rude or gracious, elated or depressed, is to relinquish control over my own personality, which has been given to me by God." He turns toward God to determine his self-worth.

One way to show our faith is to make amends and get rid of ill feelings toward other people. Begin by making a list, mentally or on paper, of any relationships that need mending. Are there people with whom you have exchanged harsh words? Are you holding a grudge toward anyone who has treated you unjustly? Have you let money come between you and a friend? Think carefully as you make your list. When the list is complete, pray that your bad feelings will disappear and that you will be able to forgive. Then meet with these people, if at all possible, and clear the air. Do not expect the other person to change. The point of contacting them is for you to offer forgiveness and friendship *unconditionally*. Even if they refuse your effort to make amends, that is all right. The important factor is for you to erase your own chalkboard and start fresh. It is vitally important to your well-being to forgive others and rid yourself of any negative feelings you may be harboring.

Kim Bergalis, a twenty-one-year-old AIDS patient who contracted the disease from her dentist, forgave him.

> I had a great deal of anger when I was diagnosed. But I honestly don't think he was in his right mind. If you know you have AIDS, why would you be in an office instead of out enjoying yourself? I don't know if my parents forgive him. I don't know if they ever will. But I have. I don't want to leave this earth without forgiving everyone who crossed my path.[15]

If it is not possible to meet with someone on your list, write a letter or make some telephone calls. If for some reason it is impossible to get in direct contact with the person because they have died or are unapproachable, you can still write a letter of forgiveness. The letter need not be mailed, only written. Forgiveness does not come from the outside; it comes from within your heart, so you will still be able to experience a complete cleansing regardless of what the outside response may be.

In addition to making amends with earthly relationships, you may need to mend your relationship with God. You may never have had a personal relationship with Jesus. Perhaps you just never felt you needed one, or maybe you never had an opportunity to pursue it. Jesus uses a parable about workers in a field to explain this. Some men worked from early morning and others showed up at various times during the day with the last group arriving and working only an hour. When the workers were paid at the end of the day, they all received the same wages. The early arrivals complained, saying they should have been paid more, but Jesus declared it was his desire to pay everyone the same wages. (See Matt. 20:1–16.) In the eyes of Jesus, all receive the same rewards regardless of the time served.

It is not too late to either begin or renew a personal relationship with the Lord. In the days ahead, it will be a great comfort to know a good friend is standing beside you as you approach the unknown. God, your refuge, "orders his angels to protect you wherever you go. They will steady you with their hands to keep you from stumbling against the rocks on the trail" (Ps. 91:11–12). With God as your constant companion you need not feel alone or afraid.

In a recent poll, statistics confirmed that God is still the most popular figure in America. The results showed that Americans spend more time in churches in one week than in all sports events combined. When questioned, nine Americans in ten say they have never doubted the existence of God. Seven in ten believe in life after death and nine in ten say they pray.[16]

When it comes to religion or faith, some people seem to have more problems accepting it. Some men seem to feel it is not masculine or "macho" to have to lean on the Lord. Others say they feel like hypocrites turning to religion only now when they are desperate.

"I never had any time for that religious stuff when I was well," one man told me. I told him that faith is like a "come-as-you-are party." Everyone is invited and it takes no special clothing or requirements. All you have to do is join in. Nobody needs to pass up the opportunity to confirm where they will spend eternity. *Eternity*—not mere days, or weeks, or months—not years, but forever and ever and ever.

To reserve your permanent spot in heaven is simple. It is a gift given freely and paid for by Jesus a long time ago. It is something anyone can afford or possess. You do not need a memorized prayer or anyone to say special words with you. All you need is a desirous heart and a sincere wish for forgiveness. "Ask, and you will be given what you ask for" (Matt. 7:7). All we need to accept this special gift is the desire to do so. A gift becomes yours when you receive it. Simply bow your head right now and, in your own words, talk to Jesus. Tell him that you believe the promises in the Bible are true. Tell him that you want to be one of his children, one of his very own. Next, confess your sins and express a desire for forgiveness. Then ask Jesus to fill your heart with the Holy Spirit and take care of you forever.

Talk to God as you would your closest friend. Tell him your needs, tell him you love him, ask his advice, and then spend plenty of time listening. It's as simple as that. Then share with someone what you have done.

Jesus said, "If anyone publicly acknowledges me as his friend, I will openly acknowledge him as my friend before my father in heaven" (Matt. 10:32).

Receiving the Sacraments

The sacraments of baptism and holy communion are available even though you are ill.

Baptism

After accepting Jesus as your Lord and Savior, you may want to be baptized as an outward sign of your new or renewed commitment. If you are still ambulatory, you may want to find a church where you feel comfortable and discuss baptism with the pastor.

Being bedbound or homebound does not mean you cannot be baptized. Simply make some telephone calls or ask a trusted person to make them for you. Most hospitals have chaplains on call or on staff who will be glad to visit you and make the necessary arrangements. Catholic priests are very comfortable with baptisms in private homes or hospitals. The churches that baptize by immersion have a bit more of a problem with the logistics, but nothing is impossible.

My friend, Charlie, came to know the Lord in the last month of his life. It was a Baptist preacher who introduced him to Jesus. Much to the delight of his family, Charlie wanted to be baptized. The pastor, however, knew only the procedure for baptism by immersion and was not quite sure how to go about it any other way. With a sudden inspiration he checked around the hospital and found a Presbyterian minister who was visiting with another patient and asked him for advice. Together the Presbyterian minister and the Baptist preacher gathered next to Charlie's bed and baptized not only Charlie but also his wife and two sons. It was a beautiful, touching moment when God's people from all different walks of life gathered as one.

Holy Communion

Holy communion is another Christian ritual that does not need to be performed exclusively in a church. Most churches have volunteers who take the sacraments to homebound parishioners. They have a special little case fitted to carry the elements and supplies. It gives great comfort to those who cannot get to church. Volunteers will usually visit anyone who is too ill to attend church regardless of whether they are active church members, non-practicing, or newly converted.

All it takes is a telephone call and an explanation of the situation to get caring Christians to visit. People should not feel it is an imposition or be embarrassed because they are not members of the church when they are requesting favors.

I have been involved in many situations with different denominations and have never received anything but a warm response and instant action. Just as Jesus responded to the lost sheep, so do committed Christians respond to those who suddenly want to join or return to the fold.

If, by chance, you do not get a positive or quick response to your needs, call back or contact another church. There are times when messages get lost, telephone numbers get copied down incorrectly, or your call gets postponed due to an emergency situation or crisis. Be persistent. The comfort you will receive from your church contacts is too important to neglect.

Charlie did not have to face the future alone and neither does anyone else. You do not have to be in a church to pray or talk to God, nor must you be in a church to be baptized or take communion. The rituals and sacraments are available for the asking. Charlie died peacefully, knowing he would be reunited with his loved ones in the future, and his wife and sons received great support from their new church family during their time of bereavement.

Saying Good-bye

When the task of making amends and forgiveness has been completed and the church contacts have been made, it may be time to get in touch with other special people in your life. Make a list of people to whom you wish to give a special message. We can get so caught up in doing laundry and getting to work on time that we forget to tell people how much we love them and we neglect to thank others for the part they have played in our lives.

Now that you have faced your mortality and are doing a thorough job of internal "housekeeping," you will probably feel a need to complete any unfinished business. Making a list on paper will help you feel more organized and will also allow you to see how much you are accomplishing in emotional tasks.

Have you told your loved ones how much they mean to you? Have you told them the reasons you find them so special? Saying "I love you" is fine, but heartfelt, personal messages are more meaningful. Messages such as "The way you smile all the time has filled my life with happiness" or "You've been such a good sport through the bad times and I really appreciate that about you" are more special.

The remarks I remember most from my deceased loved ones are not the big declarations of love, but the sincere statements that came from their hearts. One such message came from my Aunt Bea just days before she died. It was difficult for her to speak and even more difficult for her to form coherent ideas. Her expression seemed to suggest that she was going to say something profound. When she finally spoke she said, "June, I've always thought you have such a nice face."

That may not sound like a great compliment, but five years later it still touches me so deeply that tears run down my face as I write about it. If Aunt Bea had told me I was beautiful or even pretty it would have been a far cry from the truth. I would have brushed off such statements as empty compliments.

But it has always been very important to me to have people feel comfortable around me. I do not want them to feel intimidated. I want people to like me and trust me. To accomplish these goals I need to look like a nice person; I need to have a "nice face." That message must have come straight from my aunt's soul. Profound? Poetic? No, but to tell me I have a nice face is the dearest thing anyone could have said to me. It will comfort me the rest of my life and be part of a bridge between the living and the dead.

Saying good-bye can be messages of this type—plain and simple words. Your messages do not have to be articulate, fancy speeches. They need only come from your heart.

While my father was in his final illness he kept telling family members how much he loved us. When he would tell my mother he loved her, he would always add, "And I'll love you even more after I am gone." I didn't realize at the time what a loving legacy he was leaving behind until a few weeks after his death. Mom told me she could still feel Dad's love. "He loves me even more now that he's gone," she said often. Dad's oft repeated phrase continued to surface as she made her smooth transition into life without him.

My mother is now in her eighties. Since my father died, Mom and I have become very aware of how fragile life is. Therefore, we stay current on our farewells. We are not waiting for her to become ill. We have closure on every visit and every phone call. I try to remind myself to do likewise with my own children, but the urgent need is not staring me in the face as obviously with the younger generation.

Understanding Death

There are many facets of life on earth that humankind will never be able to fully understand. Along with not understanding the reasons for some people being struck down by illness, we are also unable to understand the concept of death or what happens in our next life. In a previous chapter I used the analogy of the caterpillar emerging as a butterfly.

In Scripture, Paul tries to explain life after death, with earthly bodies versus spiritual bodies, by using the analogy of a seed:

> But someone may ask, "How will the dead be brought back to life again? What kind of bodies will they have?" What a foolish question! You will find the answer in your own garden! When you put a seed into the ground it doesn't grow into a plant unless it "dies" first. And when the green shoot comes up out of the seed, it is very different from the seed you first planted. For all you put into the ground is a dry little seed of wheat, or whatever it is you are planting, then God gives it a beautiful new body—just the kind he wants it to have; a different kind of plant grows from each kind of seed. And

just as there are different kinds of seeds and plants, so also there are different kinds of flesh. Humans, animals, fish, and birds are all different.

The angels in heaven have bodies far different from ours and the beauty and the glory of their bodies is different from the beauty and the glory of ours. The sun has one kind of glory while the moon and stars have another kind. And the stars differ from each other in their beauty and brightness. . . . The bodies we have now embarrass us for they become sick and die; but they will be full of glory when we come back to life again. Yes, they are weak, dying bodies now, but when we live again they will be full of strength.

[1 Cor. 15:35–43]

Later Paul compares our earthly bodies to living in a tent:

For we know that when this tent we live in now is taken down—when we die and leave these bodies—we will have wonderful new bodies in heaven, homes that will be ours forevermore, made for us by God himself, and not by human hands. How weary we grow of our present bodies. That is why we look forward eagerly to the day when we shall have heavenly bodies which we shall put on like new clothes. For we shall not be merely spirits without bodies. These earthly bodies make us groan and sigh, but we wouldn't like to think of dying and having no bodies at all. We want to slip into our new bodies so that these dying bodies will, as it were, be swallowed up by everlasting life. This is what God has prepared for us and, as a guarantee, he has given us his Holy Spirit.

[2 Cor. 5:1–5]

I find this one of the most reassuring messages in the Bible. God has given us a *guarantee* that after death we will live on in a new and wonderful body—one that does not make us groan and sigh. I have grabbed on to this promise for my future.

Making Final Arrangements

Along with the tasks of making amends and getting legal affairs in order comes the opportunity to make known your wishes about final arrangements. Some people even choose to make their own funeral arrangements. Tom was such a person.

After the doctor told him it was just a matter of time, he drove to a funeral home and talked to the director. Then he went to two other funeral homes. He picked up price lists, went home and compared, and a few days later completed the arrangements, even paying for the services in advance.

"I don't want my family to have to do these things," he assured me. He also went to the cemetery, chose a plot, ordered a grave marker and paid for those. He did these tasks by himself and felt very good about them. As an engineer, he was an efficient, well-organized person, and this was part of his nature. He had always sheltered his loved ones from unpleasantness and that was exactly what he was doing now. When he told me about it, he never shed a tear. He reported the facts and showed me the paperwork. As my eyes brimmed with tears, I asked if this had been a difficult job for him.

"Yeah," he finally admitted, "it wasn't a lot of fun. But I'm glad I did it. It feels real good now." Then he smiled smugly, "And this way I'm sure it's been done right." I smiled in return thinking it must be his engineer outlook taking over.

Tom was a special person. Only fifty years old and putting up a real physical battle against all odds. He lived two years longer than anyone expected. During that time he was a prolific list-maker. In addition to the final arrangements, he planned his own funeral service. He spoke at length to his pastor and made it clear that he wanted a celebration of life and not a sad, depressing memorial. He wanted lively music, including "It's Only Just Begun," and a chorus of "Jesus Loves Me" sung by his grandchildren. He listed Scripture verses to be quoted and designed a program which included a black-and-white photograph of himself. On the back cover of the program with the photograph was the message, "See ya, pal," which was the way he always said good-bye.

Next, he chose the clothing he wished to be buried in and went out and bought a special striped shirt. I had to laugh when his wife told me she had finally balked and drawn the line when he wanted to choose her outfit, too. "He's just too much," she said with a grin and shook her head in disbelief.

Tom was definitely more thorough than most people and he went to an extreme. I was concerned that these plans were occupying too much of his time, but they seemed to bring him comfort. It appeared to be his way of completing his obligations on earth before preparing to depart. His family agreed that this was simply Tom's way. He had always been a very meticulous person who threw himself into every task.

About a month before he died, Tom took a turn for the worse. He called his family together and invited his pastor over for a time of fellowship and communion. The newest little member of the family was baptized right on Tom's bed and the adult members took communion together. They prayed and sang their favorite hymns while Tom's son strummed a guitar.

This may not be the way every family wants to deal with impending death, but it worked for Tom and his family. There are no rules to follow and no set procedures that need to be adhered to at this time in life. Each family and each person needs to do what he feels is best for himself. This is a family time when the heart should be the guide and protocol can be set aside.

Although Tom made all the arrangements himself, his family had a set procedure for funerals and he kept within those boundaries protecting the comfort zones of all involved. Tom checked the plans as he went along and they served the family well. He felt he saved them pain by doing it himself, and tying up loose ends gave him a feeling of accomplishment.

Tom's plans were carried out successfully. Nevertheless, there are times when the plans do not work. One of my patients insisted funerals were barbaric. "I want nothing when I go," she firmly told me and her family. "No wake, no viewing, no service, no grave. Just have me cremated and scattered. I don't want my family to have any bother or expense." We didn't argue with her.

Several months later when she died, I was called to the house. When I arrived, her son was on the telephone busily contacting funeral homes. He put together an elaborate traditional funeral complete with wreaths, a limousine, a two-day wake, a church service, and a cemetery burial. There was music and a soloist and a big reception afterward. I tried to hide my surprise as he explained, "I'm doing this for my dad and my siblings. They need it and so do I. Mom would understand." After attending the service I had to agree. The service was for the living, and Mom *would* have understood. Cost, location, the time element, and personal feelings cannot always be best determined prior to an event.

Funeral rituals are for the living. They are meant to put closure on a life that has moved on and they are an opportunity to gather together people who can offer support for the future. The hugs and love shared at a funeral are nurturing and sustaining to those who are left behind.

Decisions

Many decisions need to be made regarding final arrangements. It is especially difficult for the next of kin to make these decisions if they have no idea as to the preferences of their loved one. Every situation and every person is unique. Not everyone is like Tom, who took care of each detail himself. There is no right or wrong in this area. Do what makes you most comfortable.

Regardless of whether or not you personally take over the tasks, it is extremely important to let your wishes be known. When you let your wishes be known you are lifting a great burden of indecision and anxiety from the shoulders of your loved ones.

There are a variety of ways to let your wishes be known. You can talk openly about your choices and desires, if your family is used to handling situations in this way. If they or you are not comfortable having a discussion of this type, you can write down all the details and give the list to a trusted friend, hospice volunteer, or relative to be opened when the information is needed.

If writing is too difficult or if you feel you could express yourself more easily in conversation, try putting the information on an audiotape. I was once given an audiotape with a finely detailed message that left nothing to chance. It was received by family members with great appreciation and made their job so much easier by knowing they had carried out their loved one's intentions one hundred percent.

Pastors are generally comfortable with discussing final arrangements, especially if they will be conducting the service. Terminal patients often discuss the Scriptures they want read and the music they want sung. They may designate a special friend to assist the pastor in the eulogy. You may wish to write a personal message for the pastor to read during the service.

The choices are endless. If you have no preferences, it is just as important to let that fact be known as well. My father left a single sheet of paper with instructions numbered in the order they were to be carried out which made it very easy for us. But his most thoughtful gesture came in the postscript at the bottom of the page. He wrote, "These are my preferences, but feel free to change anything. If no preference is listed, it means I have left it entirely up to you to do what seems best." We followed most of his instructions, but when something seemed impractical or illogical we knew we had the freedom to choose otherwise and were not left feeling guilty afterward.

The following list of general items should assist you in making up your own particular list and help you become aware of some of the options. For more details or explanations of terms, turn to the Caregivers Section, *Making Final Arrangements,* on page 165.

Choices

Traditional service with visitation followed by burial
Traditional service followed by cremation
Memorial service only

Graveside service only
Speakers
Music—specific soloists, musicians, or selections
Scripture choices
Fraternal organization involvement
Person to conduct service
Clothing—formal versus informal
Obituary—any particular information to be included
Flowers or donations to specific charity
Any special message to be included in the program
Photos to be displayed
Out-of-town people who need to be notified

Financial Arrangements

If you are a veteran or are entitled to special benefits through any insurance policies or organizations, let your caregiver know how to best obtain these funds. Insurance companies have no way of knowing when they have to pay benefits unless they are notified. Be sure none of your benefits are overlooked due to lack of information. Have policies in an accessible place.

If there is a family burial plot, be sure your caregiver is informed of that detail. Try not to leave any loose ends that will cause frustrating snags or financial losses for your loved ones. If you are leaving any special instructions, be sure they will be easy to find and to follow. If you choose to actively participate in the plans, do only as much as you can comfortably handle each day. Plan your schedule around the times when you are most rested and stress-free, and ask for as much help and support as you need.

Gently remind yourself that your participation is a generous, loving gift you are giving to your loved ones.

Postscript

After the details have been settled, you can put aside the thoughts of final arrangements and concentrate on living each moment as it is. All of life is a process—a time of change and a time of growth. I have seen the healing of relationships and the blossoming of reconciliation take place following a life-threatening diagnosis.

When the days of doctors' appointments and trips for treatment are over, you can move on to other things. When the legal paperwork and financial affairs are all in order, you can relax. When you have taken care of final arrangements and have written down your preferences or discussed your wishes with a trusted person, you can feel at peace. After you have mended any broken relationships, said your formal farewells, and put your spiritual life in order, then what?

Then you simply live each moment to its fullest. You can be a loving, worthy human being as well from a hospital bed as from the head of a conference table. No matter what your physical capabilities, you can always pray, smile, and show your love. Each physical accomplishment is mere frosting on the cake. Each smile, each hug, each giggle is something to appreciate and savor. Life can be very good indeed if you take pleasure in the little things that healthy people do not even bother to notice. Look forward to the adventure ahead, swim with the current instead of struggling upstream. Allow your loved ones to wrap you in a blanket of prayers that will keep you safe and warm as you prepare to leave them.

Part Two

The Caregiver

Introduction

If we can ease a brother's sorrow
And aid him in distress;
If we can brighten his tomorrow
With deeds of kindliness;
Then we have found God's meaning
Of the word called Charity;
For when we give ourselves away
We've found life's mystery.

Author unknown
Taken from "The Short Talk Bulletin"
September 1983
Alphonse Cerza

One of the most difficult, yet most rewarding jobs a person can ever tackle is that of a primary caregiver. The primary caregiver is the person who promises to "give care" to someone, whatever it may entail, for the duration of an illness. With a terminal patient, it is not ordinarily possible to look ahead to the future when the person is cured and will be able to care for himself. Instead, the future will probably hold days filled with the process of dying, followed by a period of bereavement over the loss of a loved one.

Here in black and white that looks like a depressing, overwhelming task, but it is not. For someone to allow you to share in their last moments is a rare gift to be treasured. The months, the weeks, the days following the end of aggressive medical treatment can be the most cherished time in a person's life. This time can be one of reconciliation, of restoration, of love, and of spiritual growth. To be a part of the process of dying is as precious as being a part of the process of birth. Both are brief moments in time that are of great significance and can enrich your own life greatly. To avoid either experience is to deny yourself the opportunity to reach your full potential in earthly experiences.

4

Caring for Yourself

Your New Role

The role of primary caregiver may be entirely unfamiliar to you. Therefore, good support for yourself is vitally important. An empty vessel will have nothing to give. Caregivers must be very careful to find ways to fill their own vessels so that when they are required to pour out love, blessings, support, solace, or physical care, they have the necessary resources.

If you have ever flown on an airplane you are familiar with the flight attendant's instructions to put on your own oxygen mask before assisting anyone else. The bottom line is that if you are out of commission from lack of oxygen you cannot help your fellow man. The same goes for caregivers of patients with critical illnesses.

Taking care of yourself first is not a selfish act; it is an absolute necessity. The demands in the days ahead may be overwhelming, and to be of greatest service you must be strong and well-nourished both physically and emotionally. I am not telling you this to frighten you, but to warn you. Put on your lifesaving oxygen mask first so you are prepared to help others.

When you face an emergency with the proper protection, you stand a better chance of surviving. In the role of caregiver you will not only survive but you will also gain great knowledge, peace, love, rewards, and a profound insight into life and death. There is no other job quite like it.

Being Honest with the Patient

As you decide to accept the job of caregiver, you will need to let the terminally ill patient know you are comfortable with your new role. You must openly express your desire to stand by through whatever the remaining time will bring. Express any doubts you may have so that they can be ironed out to provide for smoother days ahead. Talk about options and who else can be called on for assistance. Discuss home care versus hospital care, letting the patient know if you are willing to be in full charge for the duration of the illness. Talk about insurance benefits and all the issues mentioned earlier in this book.

Just remember that rarely, if ever, is a caregiver asked, "How are you doing?" Yet, the patient is asked that question by almost every person who walks into his room. Caregivers are expected to have endless energy, Atlas-like strength, and no life of their own. A caregiver needs to remember that this neglect or lack of appreciation is not due to thoughtlessness; it is due to unawareness. Until someone has served as a caregiver, he or she will not understand or appreciate the role. Caregivers can offer praise and assistance to others in that role and fulfill a very real need.

In a situation where professionals are the main caregivers there will still be a friend or relative who will oversee the care, who will spend the majority of time at the bedside, and who will be most affected if the patient does not get well. In either case, the demands will be great. With a terminal diagnosis, many friends and relatives will not know what to do or what to say to either the patient or the caregiver. This results in both the patient and his loved ones feeling alone. This is the worst of times to feel isolated. Back-up help is essential; verbalize your needs and try to close the gap. Hopefully, your honesty will prompt others to come forward.

Accepting Help

I have read many articles about AIDS patients who are without any family support. The gay community is ready to step in and care for one another, setting up schedules and rotating shifts so that the patient will always have good care available. When people live with the threat of a terminal illness, they are very quick to take care of each other, not knowing if they may be the next one needing care.

Those of us not living under such tenuous conditions can more easily overlook the fact that we may someday need care ourselves. We go along blithely taking good health as a given and acting as if life on earth will go on forever. In recent years the gay community has been watching their peers die in great numbers so they no longer feel infallible or immortal. They practice brotherly love and human kindness naturally as a result of the sickness and pain that has become a part of their daily living. They have learned how to accept help and ways to ask for it. We must all try to develop these same caring skills.

It is important to be aware that you have taken on an enormous task and that you will need help, both physical and emotional, from time to time.

Recently in Fullerton, California, a two-day retreat was offered for caregivers who had been involved in twenty-four-hour care of stroke victims for many years. The title of the retreat was, "A Time to Care for Me."

One speaker suggested that caregivers stay in touch with their feelings and be honest at all times, telling the audience, "When somebody asks, 'How are you doing?' do not answer, 'Just fine,' if you are snowed under. Instead, admit that times are rough and that you could use a little help or a listening ear for a few minutes."

Another speaker advised, "Do not give up your separate existence to take care of another person every minute of every day. Continue to hang on to some separate interests, no matter how small. Any activity of your choosing done merely for yourself will have beneficial results." Do not feel selfish doing this. Think of it as another way to help your loved one.

"Some people become completely immersed in their caregiving role so they won't have to deal with their emotions. . . . It is important for caregivers to take care of unfinished business before their loved one dies so they can say, *I'm sorry* and *I love you,* but also to start the grieving process," said Bonnie Genevay, a Seattle-based counselor and consultant who spoke at the Fullerton retreat.

"Spouses must allow themselves to grieve over the loss of the dreams they shared with their mate—and the loss of touch and recognition from the person with whom they were most intimate. Working through grief frees caregivers to look toward the future with a sense not only of who they are, but who they can become. Caregivers are bound to see sorrow when they look ahead, but what about the joys and the potential?" she asked.[17]

When I was helping to care for my dad, Saturdays were my free days. My sister, Barbara, would come to help my mother and they both insisted I leave the house. Even if I did not feel like shopping, I would still head over to the mall and stroll around by myself looking in the windows. I would sit silently with my thoughts and have lunch, feeling a part of a world where people were bustling around and not thinking about bedpans, pain medication, or funerals. One time I bought a bright pink striped top and whenever I needed a lift I wore it. After my father's death I continued to think of it as my "happy shirt" and I donned it whenever I was feeling low.

After my weekly shopping trips, I would return home refreshed and ready to face another week. One Saturday it was raining fiercely and, much to Barbara's distress, I refused to leave the house. It turned out she was right and the week ahead was a rough one. It is important to recharge our batteries so we will not run out of power.

How to Avoid Burnout

1. Set achievable goals and take one step at a time so you won't be overwhelmed.
2. Learn to say no. Don't give beyond your ability to maintain your own emotional and physical well-being.
3. Pace yourself. Hurrying through tasks so you can get more done just adds to your stress.
4. Anticipate the ways in which your situation will change as your loved one's illness progresses.
5. Examine the feelings you have in response to each change so you won't be paralyzed by fear or guilt.[18]

Another way to help prevent burnout is to find a safe place to cry. Tears can express emotions in a way that words cannot. Shakespeare said, "To weep is to make less the depth of grief." Tears are a soothing release and should not be feared or dreaded. Cry with a friend if possible; crying alone denies you the opportunity to be comforted.

In addition to releasing stress by crying, go to a movie or rent a lighthearted video and have a good laugh. There is nothing wrong with taking a "laugh break." Just as tears are healing, so is laughter. The heart can only stand so much pain and sadness. Allow yourself some relief and respite.

Permit your friends to console you. This is no time for keeping a stiff upper lip or going it alone; this is a time for admitting you need help, both physical and emotional. Do not neglect your health. Remember it is vitally important to keep up your strength and good spirits. Eat well. Get some daily exercise, no matter how minimal it may be. Try to get enough sleep even if it has to be in snatches instead of in eight-hour blocks, or call in reinforcements for an uninterrupted night's sleep from time to time.

For a change in routine, invite visitors for yourself. Take time to read or be alone, admit when you feel lousy or over-burdened. The less stressed you are, the better support you will be able to offer to the patient. Treat yourself to a gift of flowers or a foamy bubble bath.

Writing

Just as talking and listening are effective devices for lowering your stress level, so is writing for both the patient and the caregiver. Often people who are unable to effectively verbalize their feelings and thoughts can put them on paper. This can be done in one of two ways: for yourself or for others.

Keeping a daily journal can help you clarify your thoughts and put your feelings into the proper perspective. Words on paper will help to keep you on solid ground when everything about you is shaky. Reading earlier entries will allow you to see your progress or help you to make decisions. Often anger can be expelled through writing in the same way that guilt or frustration can be vented.

Writing letters to others is the second way of expressing yourself when you find you are unable to do it face to face. Letters can convey news of your loved one's illness or request assistance or support when you find it is too difficult to do so in person.

If you find it difficult to talk about personal matters or to express yourself, don't hesitate to make use of this very effective tool of writing.

Networking

Another important way to avoid burnout is to network. This can help to replenish your own inner resources. One of the best ways to network is to use your telephone. Find and obtain all the support you can from information hotlines, individual illness hotlines, and support hotlines.

Check the newspaper for support groups and try to attend one if possible. Talk to social workers and hospice team members for referrals. If the patient has cancer, telephone the American Cancer Society and obtain any information on his particular type. If possible, visit the office and pick up reading material and resource information that pertains to the patient. Refer to the resource list at the back of this book and contact any suitable organizations that can assist you. And while you have the phone in your hand, call your local Social Security office and ask them to send you a copy of *Your Medicare Handbook* to check on available benefits.

Find out all you can from local hospitals, a senior center, the American Red Cross, Meals on Wheels, and errand services. Talk to any local hospice organizations to see what is available through them. If you are a member of a church, notify them of your situation and find out if they can offer help of any sort. Have your family added to their prayer chain.

Take advantage of any assistance that is available and do not be too proud to ask for help. There will come a time when you can return the good favors; allow others to assist you now when you need it. Good support can make all the difference.

To increase your coping mechanisms, Marjorie Jantz-Owens suggests the following:

1. *Schedule joy.* Be sure each day holds some fun.
2. *Step into the light.* Researchers at the National Institute of Health have demonstrated that many people suffer from SAD, a light-sensitive condition in which mood slumps coincide with the dark winter months.
3. *Add color to your wardrobe.* Color psychologist Patricia Szczerba says, "Color can be a nutrient for the mind, just as vitamins are for the body." Avoid dreary colors and atmospheres.
4. *Break up patterns.* Do something unique and exciting to liven up your routine.

5. *Seek out positive people.* Happiness and sadness can both be contagious. Surround yourself with optimists when you need a lift.[19]

And last, but not least, remember you are never alone. The Lord will be standing by your side to guide you and give you courage. I know this from personal experience. I never thought I would be able to do many of the things I have been required to do for hospice patients. With God's strong arms holding me up, I have never faltered in tasks I could not have accomplished by myself.

5

Caring for the Patient

Anyone involved with a terminally ill patient is likely to experience the same feelings the patient usually experiences. Experts have defined these feelings or stages as: shock, anger, denial, bargaining, and depression until, hopefully, acceptance is reached.

These feelings vary in each person and will be experienced at different times, with different degrees of intensity. No special order is necessary and some stages may be skipped or repeated. Whatever happens can be considered normal as long as one stage does not continue for great periods of time, cause suicidal tendencies, result in extreme depression, or cause the person to harm himself or others.

The patient and the caregiver can work out these feelings together by being open and understanding. Preferred ways to work through feelings are by talking or writing. Each person is different. Find the means of communication that serves your situation best and pursue it.

Honest Communication

Honest communication between the patient and the caregiver is vital. To help each other, both patient and caregiver are responsible for letting their needs be known and for speaking from their hearts.

Honesty should begin at the time of the terminal diagnosis. The patient will need someone to tell him exactly what is going on medically and what his options are. If the medical team has reached a point where there is nothing more they can do, when the radiation, chemotherapy, or surgery have failed to curtail the disease, it is time for someone to look at the patient truthfully and say, "There is nothing more that can be done medically. From now on, your illness is completely in God's hands." If the doctor has not done this, it will be up to someone else to do it.

Dr. Kübler-Ross asked patients to think back to the beginning of their awareness of a terminal illness.

> We asked patients if they would have been better off if they had been informed early about the seriousness of their illness, in order to give them more time to come to grips with it. The majority of our patients conveyed to us that they would have been better off if their primary physician had been honest with them at the very beginning.[20]

When I was working with hospice patients, it often fell to me to be the one to break the news. I never found a patient who was not already aware that he was dying. The usual response was one of gratitude—at last the patient could talk openly with someone about his impending death.

In actuality, the "not knowing" took more energy than accepting the truth. It is very exhausting for a sick person to keep up a brave front, and it wastes what little energy he has to pretend everything is going to be all right. When I told my hospice patients the truth, they were relieved to finally be able to talk about what needed to be done before they died. Many patients told me they were more stressed when they were wondering about their prognosis than after they were told they were terminally ill and further treatment would be useless.

> Because we are uncomfortable, we tend to gloss over the discouraged feelings of the dying. . . . If someone says, "I don't think I'm going to make it," the temptation is to reply, "Of course you will." Instead, we need to give the person the freedom to talk about their feelings. . . . A dying person needs assurances of love, help, companionship, and mutual awareness of their condition. That does not mean constant sympathy—we do not want to leave them absorbed in self-pity—but rather with continuing affirmations of well-being.[21]

It would be cruel for us to deny loved ones this last opportunity to tie up loose ends and say a final "I love you," just as it would be unfair of others to deny the truth and cheat a terminally ill person out of preparing for the most important event in their lives. We must not play protector and make major decisions when the life of another person is in such a fragile state.

In the beginning it will probably be difficult to talk about the fact that time may be limited. To be open about a terminal illness does not indicate resignation, it is merely a way of being prepared. I personally get around this by using the words "if" and "may." I make such statements as, "*If* you don't get well, what are your wishes?" or "Your illness *may* be in the last stages." We never know, for sure, that God does not have a miracle planned for us. Therefore, even though all the evidence points away from a recovery, we must hold on to hope.

I have seen two such miracles in six years. Two people, who by all medical standards should not be walking around, are living productive lives today. These were hospice patients who had seemed to be mere days from death's door. As a result, I know never to give up hope.

Listening Skills

The other half of communicating as a caregiver is asking the right questions and listening carefully to the answers. Instead of asking, "How are you feeling?" ask, "*What* are you feeling?" This lets the patient know you aren't asking about their health, but rather that you are interested in *what* they are feeling emotionally. Then be prepared to listen. Most of good communication is good listening. The greatest gift you can give the patient right now is to be a good listener.

Likewise, there is no single thing that will be harder to do. As the friend or loved one of a terminally ill person, it will be painful to listen as doubts and fears, anger, and sadness are expressed, but it is the most compassionate gift you can offer. To shut the door by responding uncomfortably with such phrases as, "Everything will be fine," or "Try not to think about it," will not help. Simply repeating empty clichés will only isolate the patient further.

Instead, use active ways of showing you care. When you hear distress in the patient's voice, stop what you are doing and offer to pray right then for the immediate problem. When my father was dying my family prayed for some rather unusual things, but the prayers came straight from our hearts and God heard them and answered them immediately. We learned that nothing was too delicate to discuss with the Lord and our faith was never as strong.

My book, *How Can I Help?*, has a section on using good listening skills when dealing with grieving people.[22] They apply equally well to terminally ill patients.

My book states that it has been established through many studies that one of the best ways to work through grief is to talk about it. (Terminally ill people are grieving the loss of life on earth.) Therefore, terminally ill people are going to need their friends to listen as they talk away their grief. I was once told that the reason I have two ears and one mouth is because I am to listen twice as much as I speak. Good advice, but not very easy to follow. Being a good listener does not come naturally to most people. It is a skill that is learned from constant practice. Anyone who wants to be able to help a person who is hurting needs to learn active, reflective, and sensitive listening skills.

Active listening is a communication technique that avoids the interference of a listener's judgment. It is understanding what is being said without imposing our own judgments, advice, or analysis on the speaker. It is a highly effective tool in situations where we want and need to understand what we are being told. It also has the added advantage of being a useful device for helping others clarify their feelings.

Active listening encourages the speaker to expand on the problem by having the listener respond with a statement such as, "Yes, go on," or "Tell me more about that."

Reflective listening goes a step further with the listener paraphrasing or "reflecting" back the statement to assure the speaker that he or she has been heard. For example, the speaker might say, "I'm too tired to even think straight." This can be paraphrased back by the listener as, "It sounds to me as though you are feeling overwhelmed and exhausted."

This is not merely parroting the speaker. When we echo the speaker before allowing the conversation to continue, it lets the person know we have heard what was said. It allows the speaker to form his next thought without the thought process being interrupted. It also provides us with necessary information to enable us to be of assistance.

If the person has trouble clarifying his or her thoughts, we can respond with, "Then this is the problem as you see it," and repeat back the information, again using paraphrases. If we are incorrect in our assumptions, the speaker can correct us, which will also help to clarify his thoughts.

Both active and reflective listening involve hearing the tone of voice the speaker is using. "I can hear that this situation makes you angry," or "You must be feeling very helpless right now." These statements encourage the speaker to expand the idea and, hopefully, to find a possible solution without the listener having to give advice. Giving advice is generally not helpful to a person who is agonizing over a situation and simply needs to talk it through.

Sensitive listening is another device that caregivers would profit from exercising. Maintain good eye contact and make physical contact with those who are pouring out their hearts to you. Show them you can accept their anger, their pain, and the depth of their feelings without it devastating you, too. Be the rock they can grab on to when waves of despair are battering them.

Remember not to judge feelings. Showing shock, disgust, or becoming defensive closes the doors to further sharing. The patient will get the message that you are unable to handle what is going on and will spare you from further confrontations with the truth. This can make the patient feel isolated and might result in depression.

Be aware that feelings are neither good nor bad, they just are. The phrase "You shouldn't feel that way" should be deleted from the English language. It is judgmental and a conversation stopper. Instead, a loving response when feelings are shared is to nod and listen while we try to understand.

Location of Care

At some point it will be necessary to discuss with the patient home care versus hospital care. Items to be considered in this decision are:

1. What is the first choice of the patient?
2. Are there one or two willing full-time caregivers available?
3. What financial coverage is available?
4. Is quantity or quality of life most important?
5. What are the feelings about resuscitation and life-support machines?
6. How about artificial feeding and hydration?
7. What about antibiotics for pneumonia or unrelated illnesses?
8. Is outside help necessary and available (social worker, therapist, hospice)?

Hospital Care

If the patient chooses to be hospitalized, look into the most convenient, most suitable facility available. Check the financial situation and gather all the facts before making any decisions. Hospital care is required when no full-time caregiver is available and the patient reaches a point where he cannot care for himself.

The dignity of the patient must be a high priority item, taking second place only to safety. Never make plans without consulting the patient and never speak down to him. Allow him to do all he can for himself and to be in charge of decision-making and choices. As a caregiver, do only what is necessary at each step along the way. As the illness progresses, your amount of involvement will increase. Never take command until it is required.

If the patient desires to be at home, but no caregiver is available, it is sometimes possible to set up shifts of numerous caregivers or to hire help. I have seen an ex-wife come back home to care for a patient. I have seen neighbors each take one day a week. I have seen relatives travel from out of town and each stay one week during the months of illness. I have seen a son from halfway across the world return home to care for his mother. Ask for help. You will not receive it until a plea has been issued and loved ones know there is a need.

Home Care

In a recent survey, four out of five people said they would prefer to die at home, though in practice four out of five people die in institutions. To die at home is to die surrounded by love. It is a time of intense closeness that can bring a family together as nothing else can. Relationships can be mended, love can be reinforced, and the patient can gain strength and encouragement from loved ones. Patients are usually more content and feel physically better at home.

> [The] continuity of home care makes it possible for the patient to know what to expect, to get accustomed to the nursing procedures, to be free of the anxiety often aroused in the hospital by the entrance of so many unfamiliar workers. At home, those who love and understand the patient have the best chance of restoring emotional balance, of evoking trust and hope, and of stimulating the patient to mobilize all his or her physical and psychological resources both to cope with stress and to cooperate.[23]

Likewise, caregivers will benefit from the opportunity to observe the end of a life at close range and to learn from it as they assist in the process. Even in a final illness we can build bridges of love that will carry us across troubled waters in the years to come.

My father and I built one of these bridges with strawberries. Dad had always loved strawberries and he had a taste for them early in the month of March. I dashed to the store, and even though they were not yet in season, I was fortunate to find some rather puny looking ones. I took my treasure home and prepared the best looking strawberry in the basket, removing the stem and setting it in the center of a fancy sherbet dish and carrying it in to him on a silver platter. How Dad's eyes lit up when he saw that single strawberry! Much to my delight, he savored the smell, the feel, and the taste of it. He smacked his lips and rubbed his tummy as he swallowed it. That single strawberry gave us both great pleasure. To this day I never prepare strawberries without thinking about Dad.

When Dad chose to die at home he gave permission to the family to share in the process of dying. It gave us time to build bridges and it gave us great pleasure to take care of him. By watching him, it took away any fear we might have had about death. It left us feeling rewarded for the care we had given him and he was much more content in his own home.

Although while Dad was sick he had very little appetite, he never refused my mother's homemade baked custard. Mom made it from scratch for him almost every day. Making the custard was one of the few ways she could satisfy her desire to cook for Dad and it made her feel useful and needed. It was one bright spot for her in each day as she lovingly prepared it. Every mouthful he swallowed was a gift to her.

In addition to the rewards, it takes great reserves of energy to care for a terminal patient around the clock; however, the rewards will outweigh the fatigue. There is no experience more intimate than to be with some- one who is facing the end of life. To be able to share in that private time and to encourage our loved one to let go gently knits families closer together than almost any other situation.

My hospice volunteers tell me that being with a per- son when he dies takes away any fear they might have had over their own deaths. They have come to see death as another chapter in the book of life, nothing fearful to be dreaded or avoided. I agree.

Sickroom Supplies

It is as easy to learn to care for a person who is ill as it is to learn to care for a newborn. Both jobs require practice, patience, and lots of love. Both chores seem insurmountable at first, but they will become easy and then indescribably rewarding. Also helpful in both situations is a good how-to manual and the advice from someone with experience, such as a hospice worker.

If the patient chooses to be cared for at home, certain items will be necessary to assure the ultimate in comfort for the patient and the ease of care for the caregiver. Medical training and skills are not necessary. There are many good books (see For Further Reading) that go into great detail on ways to set up a home hospital and care for a patient at home. The following concise list will help set up a sickroom and offer some basic suggestions for getting started.

1. Hospital beds are more comfortable for most patients and make the care easier for nurses and family members. Place bed in a central, cheerful location.
2. A bell or other means of summoning help attached to, or close to, the bed. A small inexpensive intercom made for use in a nursery.
3. A pitcher of water or juice within easy reach on a TV tray, table, or special rollaway table near the bed.
4. An "egg crate" mattress pad to help prevent bedsores. Frequent turning and repositioning are also necessary.
5. Extra pillows for propping or cushioning sensitive areas.
6. A cassette recorder close to the bed for listening to favorite music or taping messages, especially during the long nighttime hours.
7. Inspirational reading material and a Bible should be close at hand for lonely times also.
8. The old remedies such as hot tea, heating pads, and hot water bottles are still very effective, especially

to relieve anxiety. Often just changing from one position to another is distracting enough that it will relieve breathing problems caused from stress.

9. Frequent massages, and applying lotion or oil to keep skin in good condition are very soothing and relaxing when pain becomes extreme.

10. Do not force food. It is not necessary for the patient to eat.

11. Bowel movements may become sluggish due to pain medication or inactivity. Keep nurses informed as to status.

12. If patient has difficulty swallowing, liquids can be given with a large syringe specially made for that purpose. If patient can drink from a glass, a special non-spill cup with lid and spout works very well.

Physical Care

Physical care of the patient involves many factors.

Nutrition

An important part of being a caregiver will involve nutrition and mealtimes. In fact, it can be one of the most distressing aspects of the job unless the caregiver understands that the old rules about eating and nutrition no longer apply. The patient may have little or no appetite as a result of the illness or medical treatments and will resist eating. It is natural for caregivers to feel inadequate when they are unable to nourish their loved one. In turn, the patient feels guilty for making the caregiver unhappy when he cannot eat.

One of the greatest joys shared by loved ones is eating together. To give up shared delights is difficult. For the caregiver to eat alone in the next room while they think their loved one is starving is a rough situation. In my hospice work, no matter how often the nurses and I told the patient and caregiver that it was not necessary for the patient to eat, they all had great difficulty letting go of that bond. A typical situation had the wife coaxing and bribing the husband until he agreed to eat. Even if he only ate a bite or two, the wife was then happy. It made extra work for the wife, stressed the husband as he forced himself to eat, and was to no avail.

This is the time when good communication skills can help out. The caregiver can offer food, making it clear that it is not necessary to eat.

A better solution is to say, "I'll be happy to fix whatever you have a taste for if you feel like eating." Possibly suggest an item or two that may have been satisfying in the past, but make it clear that you will not be upset if the patient cannot eat.

There comes a point when the body no longer needs or wants food. Try not to make the patient feel guilty for not eating and do not take the refusal of food personally. Offer frequent ice chips and sips of liquids to prevent dehydration, but at some point those items will usually be refused also.

If the mouth becomes dry and uncomfortable and the patient requests relief, there are moisturized mouth swabs that look like oversized cotton swabs. These should be available through your health care provider or a pharmacist. Also, a moist washcloth can be sucked on or water can be squirted into the mouth with a large syringe made for that purpose if the patient requests liquid but is unable to drink. Never put anything into the mouth of a comatose or unconscious person.

I found a child's training cup with a lid and lip very helpful for my dad. He could drink at his own pace without the fear of spilling or the effort of sipping from a straw. I have since seen in drugstores these same spill-proof cups made to be used by commuters. They are larger than the training cups and done in adult motifs. Another suitable choice is the currently popular sports bottles or Sippees, which are large plastic containers with straws. These help prevent spillage and hold large amounts of liquid.

At some point nature, knowing what is best, will gradually shut down a body's system. Caregivers do not need to feel guilty for not feeding or giving drinks to a patient when he no longer desires them.

Elimination

The elimination of urine and stool is something everyone takes for granted until it stops working properly or a person cannot get into a bathroom of his own accord. Sickroom supply houses have various types of equipment to help out. One handy item is a bedside commode that can be placed near the bed. These commodes have a removable part for easy disposal and cleaning. The caregiver can assist the patient in moving from bed to commode and back again unless the caregiver is much smaller and weaker than the patient in which case there are various types of bedpans and urinals that can be used right in the bed.

Sickroom suppliers can tell you how to use them and explain the differences. Also available are pads to place under the patient to keep the sheets clean and disposable undergarments to meet almost any need when the patient can no longer get to the commode or use a bedpan.

In regard to bathroom procedures, allow the patient as much privacy as possible. Once he is seated on the commode, leave the room, if possible, and tell him to call you when he needs you. Have toilet tissue handy and allow the patient to do as much for himself as he is able.

When using a bedpan, sprinkle it with talcum powder to help it slide under the patient more easily. Again, leave the patient alone unless you are afraid he might injure himself.

Of course, all these issues are delicate and need to be handled openly and honestly. The patient must not feel like he is being a burden and the caregiver must be able to act comfortable in dealing with diaper changes or bedpans. Most people feel awkward at first, but with a little humor and lots of love they can get through it without a loss of dignity for the patient.

When food intake is decreased, elimination will also be decreased. Do not be overly concerned if the patient does not have a bowel movement every day. As long as the patient is comfortable and does not feel constipated it is okay. Stool softeners are often prescribed to keep the bowels softer when food intake is low. If any distress is present as a result of the lack of a bowel movement, be sure to tell the hospice team or contact your physician. Do not self-treat constipation with over-the-counter remedies.

Urine will decrease as liquids decrease and it may appear much darker in color. There is no need for concern unless blood is present or urine ceases completely. Any burning or unusual sensation should, of course, be reported to someone in the medical field.

Moist towelettes have many uses in the sickroom as do plastic gloves when dealing with bodily waste. The disposal of soiled garments should be done with strict regard to sanitation. Diapers should be double bagged before being taken outside to the trash, as should soiled pads that were placed under the patient, used plastic gloves, cotton swabs, and tissues. Plastic bags keep down the odor and contamination. Even when illnesses are not contagious, it is still necessary to remember proper sanitary conditions.

With the current trend stressing the issue of waste that is not biodegradable, I hesitate to write about plastic bags, nursing pads, and disposable undergarments. However, these items need to be used only temporarily. Progress is being made all the time to make these products biodegradable. I suggest you reuse plastic bags whenever possible. I have seen families save every plastic bag that comes into their home, even the bags that hold bread and frozen vegetables, and reuse them for trash disposal. Be creative, but don't sacrifice good sanitation.

Medication

Good pain control is essential. If a patient is uncomfortable, so is the caregiver. Report increased pain to the doctor or nurse and keep them informed until it is under control. Do not feel like you are being a pest. The doctor has no way of knowing that the patient is suffering unless you report it to him.

One time a volunteer reported to me that her patient was suffering terribly. The patient had been moaning and rocking with pain when the volunteer visited. The volunteer had been there only a short time when the hospice nurse arrived. The patient brightened, put on her company manners, and responded that she was "just fine." When the nurse had taken her vital statistics, written her report and departed, the volunteer asked the patient why she had not told the nurse about her pain.

"I hate to sound like a whiner," was her response.

Fortunately, the volunteer reported the incident to me and I took it back to the nursing staff. The nurse returned to the patient's house and asked the patient point-blank if she was having pain. Then the story came out. The nurse called the doctor and the medication was changed. Two days later the patient was pain-free and able to visit with her relatives who had arrived from out of town.

The American Cancer Society reports that almost fifty percent of terminal cancer patients have little or no pain. People need to be aware that cancer is not necessarily a painful disease. When pain is connected with a particular type of cancer, it is almost always controllable—but only if a medical professional is aware of it.

The patient or caregiver has the right to ask for increased doses or a change in medication. Doctors rightfully assume that everything is going along fine unless you inform them otherwise. They do not want their patients suffering needlessly. There are several pain medications on the market that can be given in conjunction with others to bring about the best relief with the fewest side effects. Do not hesitate to ask for better pain relief. As the illness progresses, pain patterns may change and the medical team will need to be kept up-to-date.

With large doses of narcotic drugs always comes the question of addiction. I once heard a hospice nurse sum it up like this, "We don't fear addiction with terminal patients. We give them as much medicine as they need. If a miracle were to occur and they got well, the pain would cease. With no pain there would no longer be a need for the drug and the dependency would be easy to reverse." Hospice workers generally agree that the fear of addiction with terminal cases is not as great as the need for comfort measures. Remember we are *caring* for these patients, not *curing* them. The most caring thing we can do is to keep them from suffering.

Home Remedies

The old tried-and-true remedies that our mothers and grandmothers used for comfort still work today. When I am feeling down, a cup of hot tea with milk soothes me. That is not because of any medicinal value; it is because my mother served me hot tea with milk when I was distressed as a child. Most families have these little tricks they can pull off a back shelf. Make use of any methods you can to alleviate pain.

Appeal to the sense of smell for enhancing tranquility. Certain fragrances may invoke happy memories. I have been in households where loved ones began baking bread just so the patient could enjoy the almost forgotten scent from his happy childhood. Cinnamon or gingerbread are familiar odors that often recall happy holiday seasons. One patient loved oranges but could no longer eat them, so the family sliced them just for her to smell. When experimenting with aromas, be sure to check with the patient first. Even if pizza used to be the patient's favorite food, the strong, distinct odor may now bring on nausea.

Just as odors can soothe, so can music. Often these "props" will bring enough relief and consolation that pain medication can be decreased or doses can be stretched farther apart.

Heating pads, ice bags, and massages with heated lotion or oil can be relaxation tools. The most convenient and least expensive ice bag is a frozen bag of peas wrapped in a towel. It has just enough weight and flexibility to mold itself to the body and stays frozen for a considerable length of time. Frozen peas cost a fraction of what ice bags or cold packs from the pharmacy cost and they can be refrozen often.

When my doctor told me about this convenient "ice bag," she reminded me to write "not for human consumption" on the outside of the bag so that the peas would not be mistakenly eaten after being defrosted and refrozen. I gave her a sly grin and asked, "Would 'do not eat' work?" Regardless of your rhetoric, mark the bag so the peas are not eaten.

Suicide and Euthanasia

The Right to Die movement seems to be gaining in popularity in recent years. A CBS poll in 1990 showed that fifty-three percent of the American people support doctor-assisted suicide.[24] Likewise, a "suicide machine" is being offered and its owner is trying to have it legalized while at the same time a book with instructions on ways to commit suicide is a best-seller.

These are signs that in recent times the importance of human beings has diminished. In our plastic, disposable society, human beings have also become disposable. "Oh, he's sick and going to die anyway, let's just get rid of him early" can become a horrifying way to look at life.

When a patient is terminally ill, depression is naturally on the scene. If the depression becomes extreme, the patient may become discouraged enough to ask for assistance or permission in committing suicide. I have encountered this twice. Both times I had a gut feeling that the patient simply needed reassurance from loved ones that they were not an overwhelming burden or nuisance. I spoke with loved ones and caregivers, explaining the situation and my feelings about it. Sure enough, when the caregiver and other loved ones reassured the patients that they were needed and loved, they stopped talking about suicide.

A terminal patient may feel unproductive because of incapacities, but even in dire illness growth is going on and life has a purpose. The growth may be spiritual where it cannot be seen or it may be the growth of a loved one or caregiver. To end life unnaturally would cause an abrupt interference with the natural growth process that God has begun before his master plan has been completed.

If your loved one should begin to express suicidal thoughts, do not act shocked. Simply treat the situation with love and openness and then look for possible underlying reasons for the extreme depression. Is medication for anxiety needed temporarily? Does current pain medication need to be decreased or increased? Is depression possibly the result of a drug reaction? Discuss all this with your medical advisors while at the same time using methods to show love and concern for the patient. This might be the time to plan a special family time with communion and prayer to lift the patient's spirit.

Lovingly give the patient a reason to hold on until the immediate wish to die recedes. Offer abundant comfort and understanding and seek professional help if you are still concerned. When a patient expresses suicidal tendencies, firmly refuse to take part in any suicide plans. Remove any possible means for the patient to commit suicide by himself. There is a big difference between allowing death naturally and causing it. You do not want to put yourself in a compromising position by assisting. Do not allow any books or information advocating active euthanasia near the patient. Stop the thought process or temptation before it takes hold and do not leave the patient unattended until the suicidal tendency is resolved.

Do not ignore talk about suicide; it is often a cry for help.

Physical Contact

One of the best ways to soothe a person is through touch. Cancer is not contagious and neither are many other catastrophic diseases, so do not be afraid to touch the patient or to express affection. Never has a person felt so fragile and needed human contact more than when fighting a life-threatening illness.

One obstacle to close contact is a hospital bed. As comfortable and as convenient as a hospital bed is, it presents problems in regard to close physical contact. First, it is higher off the floor than a regular bed. Next, it has side rails. I have found it is virtually impossible to hug or kiss a patient when the rails are up. Frequently I see patients in hospital beds with the sides up when it is not necessary. Unless there is a fear of the patient falling or endangering himself, there is no need for the sides to be up during the day and it isolates the patient needlessly.

I once had a group of volunteers do an experiment and we took turns lying in a bed to see how the patient felt. The rest of the volunteers hovered over the bed from above as people do with patients. The feeling was one of doom and claustrophobia. It made us all very aware of how it must feel to be the patient and it helped us remember to lower the rails of the bed whenever possible so we could get close to the patient preferably at his own level.

I like to sit on the bed next to my patients so we can hold hands or touch. I often see dogs and cats on the bed; I figure if they can climb on, so can I. Nevertheless, I always ask permission first and make sure it will not cause the patient any discomfort. I am cautious to hug gently and if I am in doubt about the level of pain or location of tender areas, I inquire before hugging.

Spouses should remain physically close as long as it is feasible. Sexual expression may have to change but it need not be given up completely. Plan times alone when the patient is at his best and close the door for more privacy, if necessary. If the bed is in a central location, you may have to send friends and family out for a few hours to give you some private time. One family posted a sign on the refrigerator stating, "Clear the premises every day from one o'clock to three o'clock—or else!" It worked.

The patient may be feeling unattractive due to surgery, weight loss, hair loss, or other physical changes. Reassurances and a gentle sense of humor can ease many an awkward moment. In addition to touch, there are other ways to enhance the feelings of sensuality for the patient. One is through sound and another is with smell. Soft music playing in the background makes a hospital setting seem less sterile just as pleasant aromas will enhance the atmosphere. Light a fragrant candle and let the luscious odor permeate the room with the romantic flicker of a candle flame. This is the time to use your imagination and add those special touches that will bring about feelings of peace and joy. Even the darkest hour can be brightened when you are making life more pleasant for the person you love.

When actress Gilda Radner was terminally ill with ovarian cancer, I was surprised to see so many photographs of her with her almost bald head. Ordinarily show business people are too vain to allow themselves that type of public exposure. I later read an article by her husband, Gene Wilder, where he told how cute he thought Gilda looked after her hair loss. He said he loved her "bean sprouts" of baby fine hair. Because he assured her it was sexy, she, too, was able to accept the situation and not be self-conscious of it. You can help your loved one if you make light of what otherwise seem like insurmountable physical changes.

Grandchildren love to climb in bed with their grandparents for smooches and I think it should be encouraged. It is a good learning situation for children to see that people sometimes become ill and incapacitated and the extra love from the children gives the patient a real boost.

Encourage visitors to touch, pat, and sit close to the patient. Let them know physical contact is appreciated and allowed. Often people are uncomfortable around illness and are unsure of proper behavior. It may be up to you to set the pace. An exception to getting close to the patient would be in regard to AIDS patients or others who might have a low tolerance to infection. Your health care team will advise you so you can be alert and well-informed.

Explaining Death to Children

Children should not be sheltered from the situation of illness and possible death. Include children in the care and discussions about the future to provide them with a foundation that will serve them well if tragedy strikes in their adult lives. Remember that children under six or seven years of age have a difficult time understanding that death is permanent. Television cartoons do nothing to help this concept. Children see people blown to bits and get up and walk around in the next frame. We must be very careful with our explanations and our availability to answer questions.

Word choice is important when explaining death to young children. Avoid euphemisms. Do not say a deceased person has gone to sleep, is in heaven, has become an angel, or that God needed him. These phrases can be easily misunderstood and can cause further problems. Dan Schaefer, author of *How Do We Tell the Children?*, suggests telling a child that the person got very sick and the doctors could not fix him. His body stopped working. Children understand when things cannot be fixed and stop working. This is not frightening and is within their realm of recognition. Schaefer's book is a must if there are young children involved.[25]

Terms like spirit, heaven, and eternal life are difficult concepts for adults, let alone children. The author of *Go Toward the Light*, Chris Oyler, writes how her husband, Grant, explained death to their children when they found out their seven-year-old son had AIDS.

Grant began by saying that before babies are born they are spirits. Then he used his hand and a glove to demonstrate, with the hand symbolizing the spirit. When you were born, he told their son, you were given a body. Grant put his hand in the glove showing how the spirit now had a body. He wiggled his fingers inside the glove, explaining that it was the spirit that gave the body life just like his hand gave life to the glove.

Chris Oyler explains that her children were fascinated. None of them made a sound. Before proceeding, Grant made sure they truly understood. He paused and studied each of their faces.

"And when you die," he continued, "it's as if the body just slips off again." He removed the glove from his hand and placed it on the table in front of the boys. They stared at the lifeless object.

"But the spirit continues," he said, wriggling the fingers on his hand once again. "You see, our bodies may die, but our spirits never die. Our spirits will live forever."[26] Using a visual aid, like a hand and glove, while explaining in words a child can understand, is very effective.

Children should not be shielded from funerals or final rites. Both are times of closure for children as well as adults and serve a genuine purpose. When children are included, they are able to understand the finality of death. Encourage the young people to place a flower on the grave or a note in the casket or perform some other ritual for their own personal part in the ceremony. It will be a meaningful experience and part of healthy growth. Children are more troubled by being excluded than they are by participating. Just be sure not to force a reluctant child into anything. Explain thoroughly what is going on and then let them choose if they wish to participate.

Children normally adjust well to both the process of dying and death if they are included and if the channels are kept open so they feel comfortable expressing their fears and asking questions. Watch for these simple signs that could indicate there is trouble brewing.

1. *Notice any sudden personality changes.* Something may be troubling the child that he is unable to express. Watch for an outgoing child who suddenly begins to spend a lot of time alone in his room or a shy child who becomes disruptive.

2. *Observe eating and sleeping habits.* Unexplained changes in eating, sleeping patterns, or nightmares could indicate unresolved issues that need to be talked about.
3. *Watch for changes in school work or behavior.* Inform teachers of the home situation so they can notify you if there are drastic changes at school.
4. *Listen for obsessive concern over their own health.* A discussion on details of the illness can dispel any fears about a child's health.
5. *Crying easily or being unusually stoic can indicate problems.* These can be signs of unresolved anger or guilt, or feelings that need to be expressed and given attention.

If any of these signs are present, talk with the child to find out what is going on. Seek professional help if you feel it is necessary. Above all, be honest and up front with any children who are involved. Dr. Joyce Brothers says that studies show that when children are left out or lied to, they suffer much more than when they know what to expect. Therefore, it is important to be readily available and honest. Children often feel that a parent's illness is some kind of punishment for something the child has thought, said, or done. Reassure them that illness occurs randomly and is nobody's fault. It is necessary to prepare children for impending death so that it will not be a shock when the time comes and also so they can give and receive love while there is still time. Children are amazingly resilient and deserve the same considerations as adults. They can benefit from anticipatory grief just as adults can.

Anticipatory Grief

Living with a terminal prognosis for a loved one is as painful as a gaping wound that never heals but continues to be forced open and made larger with time. You will be expected to call forth great reserves of love, energy, and endurance all the while facing the anguish of your unpredictable future. Will there be a miracle healing? Will the illness linger indefinitely or will you be left alone with your loss very soon? Loving a terminal patient forces you to face issues you may be unprepared to think about. Your choices are limited; your feelings go for a roller coaster ride.

> Death is not necessarily totally negative, and each of us, whether we are dying ourselves or comforting someone else who is dying, has resources to call upon to enrich the time that is left and to accept the end with some modicum of grace.[27]

In addition to the pain, there is one small consolation: you have been given a final gift of time to adapt. With advance warning to a loved one's final illness, you will have an opportunity to make plans, help get legal issues in order, and find out about the patient's wishes for final arrangements. You have been given the chance to say good-bye, to express your love, to tie up loose ends, to make amends.

> The increased love and compassion we can learn while caring for someone who dies . . . will help us through our initial loneliness. If the death has not been sudden, there's been time between smoothing sheets, emptying bedpans, holding hands and talking of what may come, for grieving and resolving any unclarity with the dying

person. There's been time to begin a gradual adjustment to earthly life without this person.[28]

When a death occurs suddenly, loved ones have no opportunity to prepare themselves. The shock and pain, along with unfinished business, makes the process of grief almost unbearable.

The feelings you are experiencing now—the anguish, the sadness, the anger, the yearning, and the depression—have a name, *anticipatory grief*. Being able to discuss the possibility of death with the patient before the time comes will make the adjustment afterward easier. You will have started down the path of bereavement and gotten a head start on the grief process.

6

Making Final Arrangements

Final arrangements can be made prior to a death. The book *Final Celebrations* (listed in For Further Reading) would be of great assistance in this area. Many terminally ill patients choose to make their own arrangements or to be actively involved in the plans. This is an area of great delicacy and should be handled as such. If you have a hospice organization caring for the patient, they will approach the topic and get the lines of communication flowing smoothly.

The Patient's Wishes

If you are dealing with the patient without the support of hospice, you will have to handle it yourself or ask a suitable person for assistance, such as a pastor or a friend who is comfortable discussing death. The subject can be dealt with in general terms or in complete openness, depending on whether the patient has reached acceptance or is still partially in denial.

Often a discussion on legal matters can evolve into a discussion on final arrangements. Check the section of this book on legal matters (see p. 94) and go over it with the patient. Paperwork should be put in order, insurance policy numbers should be noted, and military discharge papers and social security cards should be in an easy-to-find spot.

Another way to open the discussion on final arrangements is to inquire about the disposal of personal items. Ask, "Is there any item that you would want someone in particular to have in case you don't get well?" If the patient seems interested in this topic, suggest starting a list so there will be no confusion or mistakes. Some people choose to present the gifts themselves prior to their death. This can be a lovely gesture and gives both the giver and the recipient great pleasure.

Give deep thought to the best way to proceed with a discussion of final arrangements. Carefully use an approach that is most suitable in your situation. Choose a time when the patient is comfortable and alert and then gently approach the subject. Be sure you do not leave the patient without hope. Make it clear that this discussion is taking place in the event that the patient does not have a miraculous recovery. Do not force the conversation if the patient makes it apparent that he does not wish to discuss his own final arrangements.

However, even at times when the patient is in denial there are backdoor approaches that can be used so that the information can be obtained. You can ask, in general terms, if he thinks cremation is preferable to ground burial. You can ask about special hymns, Scripture verses, soloists, and pastors. Make notes so that when the time comes you can call on these details and put them to use. Possibly you can discuss a funeral you have attended together and get feedback in that way.

You might ask questions such as, "Did you think all the flowers at Aunt Mary's funeral were appropriate or should the money have been sent to her favorite charity instead?"

You will feel obvious when trying to get information in this manner. That is all right. The patient will probably be aware of exactly what you are doing, and that is all right, too. This allows the patient to either express his own choices or it allows him to go along with you in the only way he is able to participate at this time. It will be a bit of game-playing to make an unacceptable subject acceptable for the time being. This is not as good as an open, honest discussion, but it is much better than not dealing with it at all.

I have seen many different procedures work. Do whatever is best for your family. Sometimes the patient will take care of the details without the caregiver even having to discuss it. My dad was one of these types. Being a lawyer, he was very organized and official. Many years before his death he wrote an itemized list with every detail, numbered in the order of importance, that was to be done at the time of his death. When he became ill, he updated the list and announced to the family that it could be found in the top drawer of his desk. We never talked about it among ourselves, but we knew everything was in order. When Dad died we simply went down the list and checked items off. It was comforting to have a guide and made us feel more secure. Where Dad had no preference, he merely stated, "as per the family's wishes." I have done the same thing for my own family.

When my aunt was diagnosed as terminal, she was quick to accept her prognosis, but her husband was not. The way we dealt with his denial was to sit down and make funeral arrangements for them both, in the event that either of them died. We put everything in writing, with detailed lists, and when my aunt died everything was in good order for making decisions. We did not have to wonder about her choices.

If possible, go over the following section on choices with the patient. The major decisions will be regarding burial versus cremation, viewing the body versus closed casket, location of burial, or scattering in case of cremation. It is also helpful to know preferences as to a church service, memorial service, private ceremony, graveside service, and the denomination of the pastor. Special requests as to soloist, music, or fraternal ceremonies should also be noted. Some people have very specific desires while others do not care at all. Either way, it is best to know in advance.

Choices

Federal law requires that funeral homes quote prices over the telephone and that they have a printed general price list available. I have found funeral directors and cemetery consultants very congenial. They are generally kind, thoughtful, and easy-to-talk-to individuals.

People working in the funeral profession are accustomed to their clients being uncomfortable with the subject matter and they will make every effort to ease this discomfort. There is no reason for you to be intimidated. If you are not treated tactfully and kindly, hang up the telephone and call another one until you find someone who will communicate easily with you. Often funeral directors will mail brochures with prices or choices. Do not hesitate to ask. If you find it too difficult to do on your own, search for a friend who is comfortable doing this task. Hospice volunteers are well-qualified to take over the job. Doctors, nurses, and medical professionals are often only in the healing end of illness and are not comfortable with final arrangements. Therefore, it may be wiser to look to written material, friends, or hospice personnel for that information.

The following list touches on various choices you may be asked to make. Further explanations of terms and details follow the list.

Traditional service followed by burial or entombment
Traditional service followed by cremation
Direct cremation with burial or entombment
Direct cremation with scattering or family disposition
Direct burial
Memorial service
Graveside service
Memorial tribute

Traditional Funeral

A traditional funeral is one that has a viewing, visitation or wake, a formal service, and a burial. In addition to, or instead of, a church service, fraternal organizations may conduct the service.

The service and burial or entombment will usually take place the day after the viewing or visitation. If necessary, the schedule can be adjusted to allow for out-of-town relatives.

A funeral consultant will advise you as to your choices and provide you with a list of options and decisions that will need to be made. He will coordinate all details so the funeral will run smoothly. If arrangements are made in advance, take the time to check prices and think about details, such as using the funeral home chapel versus a church for the service. Check on your loved one's favorite Scripture verses, type of music, and choice of speakers. Try to determine if your loved one prefers a light-hearted celebration of life to a formal structured service. Does he wish the burial to be private with the only service at the graveside?

Traditional Service with Cremation

Cremation is becoming more popular for ecological and financial reasons. It is a practical method and is used by many families. Cremation with a traditional service does not grant the monetary savings that a cremation with scattering does.

With a service and cremation, there is still a viewing and visitation period and a casket is purchased. The cremation takes place following the service and the burial or scattering is done at a later date either privately or with only close family members present.

Memorial Service

A memorial service is usually held without the body or cremains being present. It can be held even weeks after the death if necessary or desired. This is suitable if many people have to travel from out of town or in case of a service held in a different location from where the deceased was residing. Often in case of cremation a memorial service is held.

Disposition of Cremated Remains

Cremated remains are stored in an urn. The urn is a box-type container of various styles and price. The choices usually include hand-carved oak finishes, marble, or brass. Prices range from about $25 to $400. The urn can be buried in the ground just as a casket would be, placed in a niche (a drawer-type place either inside a building or outside), kept by a loved one, or scattered wherever it is legally allowed.

Be aware that there are many laws and restrictions on scattering. Check your options carefully so that no last minute hitches will occur. Scattering is not as popular as it used to be and almost fifty percent of the families are opting for burial. In the past, I have personally heard many people lamenting because there was no special spot to visit following a scattering. Cemeteries are counteracting this problem by having rose gardens for scattering. This works well because it gives the bereaved a peaceful place to visit and meditate.

If a memorial service is desired, the urn may or may not be visible during the memorial service. Often an enlarged photograph of the deceased is on display. A private interment may take place at the cemetery or the burial may take place without family members present.

Direct Burial

A direct burial is almost as inexpensive and simple as a direct cremation. It involves no embalming or casket and can be done quickly and privately. It is suitable if no viewing or visitation is desired or if there are no remaining family members to attend a funeral. If desired, a memorial service and gathering of friends can take place without visitation.

Burial

The most common place for burial is a cemetery. Some states allow burial on private property as long as a permit is filed properly with the county or state. People who own large plots of land often like to have their loved ones buried "at home." This may take some advance notice and filing of paperwork, so look into it in advance.

Cemeteries, like funeral homes, offer varied choices and have a wide price range. They are not required by law to have a printed price list or quote prices over the phone. Nevertheless, I have found the staff at cemeteries to be very helpful and never had a problem getting prices and options by telephone.

The primary choices are between ground burial for casket or cremated remains, mausoleum for either, or a niche or scattering for cremated remains. Often cemeteries will let you place a plaque on a tree or purchase a bench with a plaque if cremains have been scattered. I have seen walls with memorial plaques where no burial took place. A popular new burial method is called double-depth plots. These are for two people and the cost is considerably less than two separate plots. A single plot can contain six cremated remains for families who all want to be buried in one spot. Again, the savings are considerable.

Anyone who has served in active military duty and has been honorably discharged is entitled to a marker from the government for a nominal fee. No reimbursement is made on markers that have already been purchased. You must get the original marker from the Veteran Affairs office in your county, so notify them as soon as possible.

There are many choices in markers from marble to bronze, small to large, single, double, or family. Most cemeteries no longer allow headstones, but require a flat marker. You may desire a special message on the marker or a symbolic sign from a fraternal organization.

Perpetual or Endowment Care

One additional item that can usually be included in the burial arrangements is the continued care of the grave site for a reasonable one-time charge. It is especially important in situations where no family members reside near the cemetery.

Cost and Payment

The fact that funerals can involve large amounts of money is no secret. Most of us have heard the tales of families who went so far overboard on an impressive funeral that the entire insurance benefits were used up to pay it off.

This is not necessary. I do not think any of us would want our loved ones going into debt over a flashy or elaborate funeral. I know one young couple whose baby died at birth who spent $8,000 on her funeral. It took them five years to pay off the loans and the young woman had to drop out of college to help make the monthly payments.

Most funeral expenses must be paid at the time they are incurred. Pre-need (made before the death) arrangements are becoming more popular. The payments can be spread out for up to five years or until the time of death, whichever comes first. Under almost all circumstances, the funeral and burial bills must be paid twenty-four hours beforehand. If you are planning to use life insurance benefits, check into it. Funeral homes do not like to count on insurance companies, and chances are good that you will be required to pay before the benefits arrive. This is another reason for keeping the costs within your means. A few simple advance telephone calls can keep matters straight and save undue stress later on.

The Personal Touch

Many people are getting away from customs and traditions. They are having funerals that are more personal and a tribute to the individual's life-style. The personal touch brings a familiar warmth to the coldness of a funeral and goes a long way in adding solace.

In religions where strict rules need not be followed, music can be playing, candles can be lit, flowers and special items may be placed about the room. The star of the football team may be buried in his letter jacket with a football tucked under his arm. A soldier may be buried in full dress uniform wearing his military boots and carrying his rifle. A cowboy can wear his plaid shirt, blue jeans, and favorite hat. Children are buried with stuffed toys and with letters from their siblings tucked beside them. One grandmother was buried in her fuzzy pink slippers and a soft, faded pink flannel nightgown. People can choose what feels right to them.

The most unusual funeral I experienced was held for a young man who played the drums with a band at night and was an animal trainer during the day. Surrounding his casket at the cemetery were six fellow animal handlers with large trained felines. Off to the side was his band. They played jazz music as the large felines sat at attention.

The final tune was "When the Saints Go Marching In." It was the perfect send-off with red, white, and blue helium balloons released as a grand finale.

Military personnel are entitled to a military funeral. It takes but a phone call to the Veterans of Foreign Wars or a local military facility to line up a bugler and chaplain who will do the service gratis. A marker will be provided for the grave for a small fee and there will be a flag draped over the casket that is folded and presented to the next of kin as part of the service.

Fraternal organizations usually have ceremonies or rituals they perform for their members. A few phone calls should give you the necessary information. Pianists and soloists are best found through churches that usually have a list of their musicians who would be willing to assist with a funeral.

Some nice touches I have seen are poster boards with a collage of photos from a person's life including baby pictures, wedding pictures, and highlights of happy events. Sometimes just a single enlarged photo is on display near the guest book. Pictures can be displayed whether the casket is open or closed. I have seen entire funeral services videotaped and professional photographers snapping pictures for those who could not be present. All these details are a matter of choice. What is acceptable and appropriate for one family may not work for another. Do whatever serves you best.

The funeral home will provide a guest book and other items such as programs or memorial bookmarks imprinted with a Scripture verse or poem. At the time the arrangements are made they will tell you what is available. Do not be afraid to ask about cost.

Following the burial, most people share in a meal. Friends, neighbors, or church families often provide the meal at the home or at the church. Some families go to a favorite restaurant or have a catered affair. This can be a wonderful time of giving and receiving solace. It can be a celebration of a life and a time of reinforcing love.

Following a death there are often people who will need to be notified. They may be people who live far away or who were personal friends of the deceased who communicated infrequently. They may not have even been aware the person was ill. A short card or photo-copied note gently stating the facts can be sent to out-of-towners after the death has occurred. Some families include the program from the memorial service or funeral or a family photograph. A good place to locate the names and addresses for these people is in a Christ-mas card record book or a personal address book.

The Obituary

An obituary can be written by a close friend or fam-ily member and submitted to the local newspaper. Some people prefer to write their own. If possible, find out what your loved one feels has been most important in his life so that can be included. Possibly a special friend could be mentioned along with relatives.

One man wanted his dog, Spike, to be included with his loved ones. Often, what we are most proud of in our lives is not the same as what others consider our great-est accomplishments. For example, being an author does not play as great a role in my life as being a mother; winning a writing contest is not as important to me as having been married for over thirty years. I plan to write my own obituary so that like Tom, who made his own final arrangements, I'm sure it is done right.

Now is also the time to find out if donations to a favorite charity are preferable to flowers. The obituary should include this information.

Tribute Programs

The latest addition to funerals are Tribute Programs. They are offered through some funeral homes and involve a personal videotape. For instance, one made for a ninety-two-year-old woman named Sarah opened with a baby picture and included family pictures, along with school pictures and views of the old family ranch. There were shots of old photos and of ducks floating on a pond, interspersed with a wedding picture and one of grazing horses at sunset. There were pictures of Christmases past and of Sarah lovingly holding her children and grandchildren. The final picture was of five generations all gathered around ninety-year-old Sarah at her last birthday party. There was appropriate background music, but no narrative. The pictures told the entire story by themselves.

I have been impressed with all the tribute videos I have seen. They are uplifting, not depressing, and would make nostalgic viewing for many years to come. I can see these being used to show grandchildren who are too young to remember Grandma or what her life was all about.

Understanding Death

Death is a difficult concept for children and adults alike. I am asked many questions for which there are no answers. In an attempt to at least come up with some personal opinions, I have done extensive reading and research on the subject of death.

I have read many books on Near Death Experiences and I have talked to many people who have had such experiences. Although there are no firm answers, the usual consensus is that death is not to be feared. I am told by those who have been declared dead and been brought back that there are no words to describe the feelings of peace and love that surround Near Death Experiences.

I searched for something more concrete than the analogy of a caterpillar turning into a beautiful butterfly but nobody could seem to adequately verbalize the experience.

I have delved into Scripture for reassurances and promises. My favorite is First Corinthians 15:35–50 which compares the body we were born with, made from dust like Adam's, and the new body we will be given after death.

"Someone may ask, 'How will the dead be brought back to life again? What kind of bodies will they have?' What a foolish question, (Paul says). You will find the answer in your own garden."

Paul goes on to describe a seed that is put into the ground and then sprouts up with an entirely different look. A dried-looking seed buried in the ground bursts forth, green and full of life. It goes on to grow and produce. To explain how the process comes about is impossible. We simply must have faith that the seed will fulfill its promises after it is planted. (See page 113 for more details.)

After the final arrangements have been discussed, the desires of the patient are clear, and the necessary plans have been made, you can share whatever time is left in an atmosphere of peace and love.

Signs of Approaching Death

As the patient becomes sicker, the systems of his body will begin to shut down. There are certain symptoms that are often present during the last couple of days of life. Being conscious of these signs can help you prepare for approaching death. Even though you have been caring for the patient and discussing the possibility of death, it can still be a shock when the time actually comes. By being tuned in to the physical changes, you can be better equipped emotionally.

Not all symptoms will be present in every patient and some may not be experienced at all. Patients often slip into a comatose or semi-comatose state for one to three days prior to death and others can take a final breath in the middle of a sentence. The following list is adapted from one used by the Antelope Valley Visiting Nurses Hospice Organization.

Signs of Approaching Death and What To Do To Add Comfort

If the patient begins to sleep more and is difficult to awaken it can be the result of metabolic changes.

Plan activities and communication at times when he/she seems more alert.

You may notice your loved one having confusion about time, place, and identity of people. This is also the result of metabolic changes.

Gently correct the patient, but do not be unduly concerned about the confusion.

Loss of control of bowel and bladder may occur.

Place pads under the patient. Ask your medical professional about the appropriateness of a catheter.

Arms and legs may become cool to the touch and the underside of the body may become darker as circulation slows down.

Keep the patient warm with extra blankets.

Secretions may collect in the back of the throat causing noisy breathing. This is often called the "death rattle." It can go on for days.

Use a cool humidifier in the room. Elevate the head of the bed or add extra pillows. Moisten the mouth with ice chips, or a moist washcloth if the patient is able to swallow. Reposition patient onto side.

Hearing and vision will lessen as the nervous system slows down.

Keep lights on in the room. NEVER assume a patient cannot hear. Talk as if hearing is intact and be very cautious about side conversations in the room.

There may be restlessness, pulling at bed linens, having visions, calling out.

Stay calm, speak slowly and assuredly. Do not leave the patient alone if they are showing signs of distress.

As the result of dehydration, a sweet odor may be present.

Keep the premises as clean and well-aired as possible without chilling the patient.

After the Death

When a death takes place at home, the caregiver will be in charge. It is not necessary to rush around and do anything. Instead, try to stay calm and console anyone else who is present.

Many families wish to bathe their loved one, change their clothing and bedding, and gather special people together to say farewell in the privacy of a familiar environment.

I have been in households where the pastor and family members were called and they all spent time in prayer before calling the funeral home to take their loved one away to be prepared for a formal funeral.

I have seen a wife trim her deceased husband's beard before notifying the funeral home and I even had two daughters insist on photographs with their dad before he was taken to be cremated. People may wish to cut off a lock of hair or sprinkle a favorite perfume on the body. All these acts are fine.

Do not worry about anyone judging what you do. Each death is a unique experience and you must be true to your natural reactions. Spending quiet time and saying a final good-bye can ease the pain of separation and begin the grief process in a normal, natural manner. There is no rush to have your loved one removed from your home. This may be your last private time together so use it productively. It might take three or four hours to gather loved ones who wish to say private good-byes, and that's all right too.

Years ago families handled funerals at home without professional assistance. The male members built the wooden casket and the women prepared the body. The children were on the scene helping when necessary. The wake took place in the parlor and the burial was often in the far pasture. Today, we have professionals handle the details and we deny ourselves the feeling of natural closure.

Often loved ones are at loose ends after a funeral, feeling left out and wondering, "Is this all there is?" Taking your time and being ready to turn your loved one over to professionals will insure that you are prepared to let go.

If you are working with a hospice organization they will have given you instructions not to call 911 but to call them instead. If you are not working with hospice, look into the necessary procedure to follow for your city or county beforehand. You will want to prevent getting delayed with the coroner's office or having to call a medical examiner in the middle of the night. Ask your physician what the best procedure is and check with the fire department or coroner's office ahead of time.

Often a signed statement from a physician declaring the patient is terminally ill will suffice and allow resuscitation measures to be omitted. When a hospice organization is involved, the nurse will come out and pronounce the patient dead and later take the death certificate to the physician for his signature. She will help prepare the body and call the funeral home. She will be a soothing, experienced influence who can take charge. If hospice is not on the scene someone else will need to take over this job and organize matters.

Thinking about the time of death and planning for it is not weird or morbid. It is a necessary task—a time of preparation that will make the actual moment less stressful and emotional. It will save confusion and chaos and bring loved ones together to support each other and ease the pain.

Many months are spent in planning for the birth of a baby. The mother and father plan and prepare for the arrival so that it will go smoothly and be a meaningful time. Death is the other end of life's picture. It is just as natural as birth and an inevitable moment for each of us. By thinking about it and making necessary decisions in advance, it can be a time of reinforcing love and making a natural transition.

Bereavement

Grief is the emotional response to a loss. Bereavement is the period of time following a major loss. If you have been the main caregiver during a terminal illness, you will be at loose ends for awhile. Be aware that you will not always feel as you do now. Take your time as you tenderly ease yourself back into activities you enjoyed before becoming a caregiver.

Grief demands much energy and cannot be rushed. The adjustment will take time, so do not expect to jump back in to normal activity overnight. The best therapy for grief is talking about your feelings. The second best is writing about them. Do one or the other or both until you feel good again. Don't try to rush your feelings.

Sandra Aldrich, a few years after her husband died, writes,

> As I analyze all that's happened in these past few years, I confess I'm a different—perhaps even better—person

because of the traumas. Not only do I see the hurts of others now, but I've learned to embrace the joy in this moment.[29]

If you feel relieved following the death of your loved one, do not feel guilty. This is a normal reaction after a long illness. It is natural to feel relief that your loved one is no longer ill. You may be exhausted or feel frazzled after months of giving care, and relief that the situation has changed is also perfectly normal.

Try to simply live one day at a time and do not make elaborate plans too far in advance. Read some good books on grief (see For Further Reading); join a support group if you feel you need one. Spend time with friends doing enjoyable activities. Laugh, swim, and eat luxurious meals. Buy a new outfit, go to the mountains and build a snowman. Just enjoy each hour of each day, remembering to treat yourself gently. Take it easy and do a lot of pampering. Lower your expectations. Spend quiet time in prayer, simply letting the Lord soothe and nourish your soul.

People who have had the privilege of caring for their loved one during a final illness will find rewards that far outweigh the pain. There will be happy memories to review and a feeling of accomplishment. Look into your lap at your hands folded in prayer and know that they gently guided your loved one home. You have given an irreplaceable gift of love to someone and can feel good about it for the rest of your life. Embrace that thought and let it console you in the days ahead.

Notes

Chapter 1. The Physical Aspect

1. Lois Wyse, *Kid, You Sing My Songs* (New York: Crown Publishing, Inc., 1991), p. 83.
2. Elisabeth Kübler-Ross, *Living with Death and Dying* (New York: Macmillan Publishing Co., 1981), p. 48.
3. Deborah Duda, *Coming Home* (New York: Aurora Books, 1991), pp. 99–100.
4. Frederick J. Meyers, M.D., "A University-Based Hospice: An Effective Program for Pain Management Education," U.C. Davis School of Medicine.
5. Amy M. Orser, "The Creative Arts in the Hospice Setting," *Thanatos*, Fall 1991, p. 9.
6. Felicia E. Halpert, "The Danger of Medication Mix-ups," *Parents*, April 1991, p. 185.
7. Ralph L. Klicker, M.S., "AIDS: A Look at the Disorder," *Thanatos*, Summer 1989, p. 18.
8. Laura Miller, "How to Let More Pleasure into Your Life," *McCalls*, August 1991, p.126.
9. *People*, "Why Did Gilda Die?" June 3, 1991, p. 81.

Chapter 2. The Emotional Adjustment

10. Elisabeth Kübler-Ross, *Death: The Final Stage of Growth* (New Jersey: Prentice-Hall, 1975), p. 164.
11. H. Norman Wright, *Beating the Blues* (Ventura, Calif.: Regal Books, 1988), p. 7.
12. Elisabeth Kübler-Ross, *AIDS* (New York: Macmillan Publishing Co., 1987), p. 167.
13. Deborah Duda, *Coming Home* (New York: Aurora Books, 1987), p. 58.

Chapter 3. The Spiritual Approach

14. Randy Becton, *Everyday Strength* (Grand Rapids: Baker Book House, 1989), p. 13.

15. Scott Eyman, "Finality, Putting a Brave Face on Dying," *Antelope Valley Press*, Cox News Service, April 25, 1991.

16. Gary Wills, "The Things That Matter," *Reader's Digest*, May 1991, p. 84.

Chapter 4. Caring for Yourself

17. Sherry Angel, "Care-Givers Often Neglect Somebody: Themselves," *Los Angeles Times*, May 22, 1991.

18. Ibid.

19. Victor M. Parachin, "From Sad to Glad," *Standard*, May 1992.

Chapter 5. Caring for the Patient

20. Elisabeth Kübler-Ross, *Living with Death and Dying* (New York: Macmillan Publishing Co., 1981), p. 24.

21. E. Langston Haygood, "Death," *Discipleship* Journal, Issue 62, 1992.

22. June Cerza Kolf, *How Can I Help?* (Grand Rapids: Baker Book House, 1989), pp. 89–91 (paraphrased).

23. Lois Barclay, *The Home Hospital* (New York: Basic Books, Inc., 1982), p. 14.

24. *Family Voice*, Feb. 1992, Vol. 14, #2, (Washington, D.C.), p. 4.

25. Dan Schaefer, *How Do We Tell the Children?* (New York: Newmarket Press, 1988).

26. Chris Oyler, *Go Toward the Light* (New York: Harper & Row, 1988), p. 151.

27. Elisabeth Kübler-Ross, *Living with Death and Dying* (New York: Macmillan Publishing Co., 1981), p. 97.

28. Deborah Duda, *Coming Home* (New York: Aurora Books, 1991), p. 12.

Chapter 7. Understanding Death

29. Sandra Aldrich, *Living Through the Loss of Someone You Love* (California: Regal Books, 1990), p. 117.

For Further Reading

Caregiver

Death and the Caring Community by Larry Richards and Paul Johnson, M.D. Portland, Oreg.: Multnomah Press, 1980. Compassionate information on ways to express God's love to the dying and aid in the process.

Final Gifts by Maggie Callanan and Patricia Kelley. New York: Poseidon Press, 1992. Understanding special awareness needs and communication of the dying.

Kid, You Sing My Songs by Lois Wyse. Copyright Garret Press, Inc., New York: Crown Publishers, Inc., 1991. Insightful reflections from a recent widow about her husband's terminal illness and her acceptance and adjustment.

When Someone You Love Is Dying by Norma Upson. New York: Simon & Schuster, 1986. Handbook for counselors, family and friends of a dying person. Discusses numerous aspects of caring for the terminally ill.

Children

Explaining Death to Children by Earl Grollman. Boston: Beacon Press, 1965. Practical information for dealing with children and death.

Go Toward the Light by Chris Oyler. New York: Harper & Row, 1988. Insightful information by the mother of a seven-year-old with AIDS, his diagnosis, illness, and death.

How Do We Tell the Children? by Dan Schaefer and Christine Lyons. New York: Newmarket Press, 1986. An honest step-by-step guide to help children understand death and grief.

General Information

AIDS by Elisabeth Kübler-Ross. New York: Macmillan Publishing Co., 1987. Case histories and information about dealing with AIDS.

Beating the Blues by H. Norman Wright. Ventura, Calif.: Regal Books, 1988. Christian approach to overcoming depression and stress.

The Cancer Conqueror by Greg Anderson. New York: Andrews and McMeel, 1988. Written as a parable, traces one man's journey from fear and futility to a calm, controlled, accepting view of cancer.

Everyday Strength by Randy Becton. Grand Rapids, Mich.: Baker Book House, 1989. Inspirational help for cancer patients written by a cancer patient.

Final Celebrations by Kathleen Sublette and Martin Flagg. Ventura, Calif.: Pathfinder Publishing, 1992. A guide for personal and family funeral planning.

For Better or For Worse by Beverly Kievman with Susie Blackmun. Chicago: Contemporary Books, 1989. Valuable information about a couple dealing with chronic illness.

Living with Death and Dying by Elisabeth Kübler-Ross. New York: Macmillan Publishing Co., 1981. Case histories and information on dying with dignity and grace.

No Time for Nonsense by Ronna Fay Jevne, Ph.D., and Alexander Levitan, M.D. San Diego: LuraMedia, 1989. Positive and realistic information for getting well against all odds.

The Road Back to Health: Coping with the Emotional Aspects of Cancer by Neil A. Fiore, Ph.D. Berkeley: Celestial Arts, 1990. Positive advice for fighting cancer and sustaining a hopeful attitude.

When Is It Right to Die? by Joni Eareckson Tada. Grand Rapids, Mich.: Zondervan, 1992. Discusses moral, emotional, philosophical, and spiritual issues surrounding euthanasia.

Grief

Grief Recovery by Larry Yeagley. Self-published, 1981. Can be ordered direct, 1055 Horton Rd., Muskegon, MI 49445. Excellent information in easy-to-understand style.

Life After Loss by Bob Deits. Tucson: Fischer Books, 1988. Practical steps for working through grief.

Living Through the Loss of Someone You Love by Sandra Aldrich. Ventura, Calif.: Regal Books, 1990. A widow's personal story of loss, grief, and newfound hope.

When Will I Stop Hurting? by June Cerza Kolf. Grand Rapids, Mich.: Baker, 1987. Addresses the emotions experienced following the loss of a loved one and offers help and hope for the future.

Survival Guide for Widows by Betty Jane Wylie. New York: Ballantine, 1982. Practical information for women living alone. Includes advice on finances, emotions, children, and spirituality.

Life After Death

Facing Death and the Life After by Billy Graham. Waco: Word Books, 1987. Discusses death realistically with confidence that faith will conquer it.

Life After Life by Raymond A. Moody, Jr., M.D. Carmel, N.Y.: Guideposts, 1975. Case histories of people who have been clinically dead and survived to tell about their Near Death Experiences.

The Light Beyond by Raymond A. Moody, Jr., M.D., with Paul Perry. New York: Bantam Books, 1988. Case histories and information on the study of Near Death Experiences, especially those of children.

Reflections on Life After Life by Raymond A. Moody, Jr., M.D. Boston: G. K. Hall, 1978. Follow-up and explanations of previous volume.

Nursing

Caring for Your Own by Darla J. Neidrick, R.N. New York: John Wiley & Sons, Inc., 1988. Medical advice, illustrations, equipment descriptions for home nursing.

Coming Home: A Guide to Dying at Home with Dignity by Deborah Duda. Aurora Press, 1987. Can be ordered from Aurora Press, Box 573, Santa Fe, NM 87504. $14.95 + $2.00 s/h.

The Complete Guide to Home Nursing by Diana Hastings. London: Barrons, 1986. Describes nursing care in great detail with illustrations. Includes a section on first aid.

The Doctor's Book of Home Remedies by the editors of *Prevention Magazine* Health Books. Rodale Press, 33 E. Minor Street, Emmaus,

PA 18098. Contains hundreds of home remedies that can give comfort easily and inexpensively.

Easing Aches and Pains by the editors of the *Prevention Total Health System*. Rodale Books, Box 8, Emmaus, PA 18099-0008. Natural methods for relieving pain.

Extended Health Care at Home by Evelyn M. Baulch. Berkeley: Celestial Arts, 1988. A complete, practical guide to home nursing.

Home Care, A Guide to Family Nursing by Jane Henry Stolten. Boston: Little, Brown, 1975. Help for home nursing care.

Home Health Care by JoAnn Friedman. New York: Norton, 1986. Guide to nursing done at home.

The Home Hospital by Lois Barclay Murphy. New York: Basic Books Inc., 1982. Detailed information on home nursing.

Hospice, A Caring Community by Theodore Koff. San Francisco: Jossey-Bass, 1988. The hospice theory explained.

A Hospice Handbook by Michael P. Hamilton and Helen F. Reid. Grand Rapids, Mich.: Eerdmans, 1980. A guide to help evaluate if hospice care is appropriate.

The Hospice Movement—A Better Way of Caring for the Dying by Sandol Stoddard. New York: Random House, 1978. The history and philosophy of the hospice movement.

The Hospice Way of Death by Paul M. Dubois. New York: Human Sciences Press, 1980. The theory and philosophy of hospice.

Periodicals

American Cancer Society
777 Third Avenue
New York, NY 10017
(212) 371-2900
Numerous brochures, booklets, and educational material for cancer patients. Practical information on nutrition and care of the terminally ill.

Local IRS office
Publications on inheritance taxes (both federal and state) and tax information for survivors.

National Cancer Institute
Bldg. 31, Room 1018
Bethesda, MD 20892
1-800-638-6070
Many written resource materials.

National Hospice Organization
Suite 901
1901 N. Moore Street
Arlington, VA 22209
(703) 243-5900
Good assortment of publications.

Thanatos Magazine
Quarterly publication sponsored by
National Hospice Organization.
PO Box 6009
Tallahassee, FL 32314
Publication with a wealth of information on death and grief.

Organizations

In case of suicide threats:

American Psychological Association (202) 955-7600

American Psychiatric Association (202) 682-6000

National Mental Health Association
1021 Prince St.,
Alexandria, VA 22314-2971
(703) 684-7722

Salvation Army and The Samaritans in local directories

Suicide prevention hotline 1-800-444-9999

AARP Widowed Persons Service
1909 K Street NW
Washington, DC 20049
Assistance for senior citizens.

AIDS National Hotline
1-800-342-7514
Recorded information 24 hrs. a day.

AIDS Quilt
(The Names Project)
1-800-USA-NAME or 1-800-872-6263

CancerCare
1180 Avenue of the Americas
New York, NY 10036
(212) 302-2400

Cancer Information
1-800-4-CANCER

The Candlelighters
1312 18th St. NW, Suite 200
Washington, DC 20036
1-800-366-2223
Childhood Cancer Foundation

Caring Cancer Ministry
PO Box 1315
Abilene, TX 79604
(915) 673-4352
A non-profit ministry run by volunteers for people with life-threatening illness. Run by Randy Becton.

Casa De Esperanza
Box 66581
Houston, TX 77266
(713) 529-0639
Non-profit program that assists in caring for children with AIDS. Special homes for children staffed by volunteers.

Children's Hospice International
(703) 684-0330

Children with AIDS Project of America
1-800-866-AIDS

Christian AIDS Services Alliance
PO Box 23277
Washington, DC 20026
(410) 268-3443
A national referral network of ministries, agencies, and churches.

City of Hope
1500 E. Duarte Road
Duarte, CA 91010
1-800-826-HOPE

The Compassionate Friends
Box 1347
Oak Brook, IL 60521
(708) 990-0010
Grief support for loss of a child.

Corporate Angel Network
Westchester County Airport
Building 1
White Plains, NY 10604
(914) 328-1313
Financial assistance for cancer patients.

Dial Nutrition
1-800-366-1655
Toll-free hotline at the National Center for Nutrition and Dietetics.

Exodus International
PO Box 2121
San Rafael, CA 94912
(415) 454-1017
A referral organization that can put you in touch with a ministry
in your area.

FIND, write Guideposts Outreach Ministries, PO Box 855, Carmel,
NY 10512-9971. If you have a special need and cannot find the right
organization or agency to help you, contact FIND.

General AIDS information
1-800-342-2437
Referrals, test centers, and free literature.

The Good Grief Program
Judge Baker Children's Center
295 Longwood Avenue
Boston, MA 02115

Promotes coping and prevents the development of emotional symptoms and problems in groups of children who are at risk because of a recent death or terminal illness of a friend.

Grief Recovery Helpline
1-800-445-4808

1-800-HIV-INFO hotline
Calls can be anonymous. Information on ways to stay healthier and strengthen your immune system through the development of positive attitudes, proper diet, moderate exercise, and stress management.

HOSPICELINK
1-800-331-1620
Directory of hospice services that are available and short-term telephone support.

Human Service Alliance
3983 Old Greensboro Road
Winston-Salem, NC 27101
(919) 761-8745
A volunteer organization that offers a wide variety of opportunities for full-time live-in services.

Leukemia Society of America
600 Third Avenue
New York, NY 10016
(212) 573-8484

The Life Center of the Suncoats, Inc.
214 S. Fielding Avenue
Tampa, FL 33606
(813) 251-0289
A non-profit organization dedicated to providing free counseling, education, and group support for people with serious illness or who are grieving the death of a loved one.

National Center for Nutrition and Dietetics
216 W. Jackson Blvd.
Suite 800
Chicago, IL 60606-6995

National Hospice Organization
Suite 901
1901 N. Moore St.
Arlington, VA 22209
(703) 243-5900

Physician Data Query
Building 31, Room 10A18
Bethesda, MD 20205
1-800-4-CANCER
Computer printout of experimental cancer programs. Call National Cancer Institute and ask for a copy.

Rainbows for All God's Children Headquarters
(708) 310-1880
Services and support for children with catastrophic illnesses.

Reyes Syndrome hotline
1-800-233-7393

Ronald McDonald House
(212) 876-1590
Home-away-from-home for children with serious illnesses.

Social Security Office
1-800-772-1213
Call for a Medicare handbook to check on available benefits.

The St. Francis Center
5135 MacArthur Blvd., N.W.
Washington, DC 20016
(202) 363-8500
A source of guidance, information, and support for people living with a life-threatening illness.

The Sunshine Foundation
2001 Bridge Street
Philadelphia, PA 19124
1-800-767-1976
"Bringing sunshine into the lives of seriously ill children."

TOUCH
513 Tinsley Harrison Tower
University Station
Birmingham, AL 35294
(205) 934-0368
Support for cancer patients.

Veterans' Benefits
Superintendent of Documents
U.S. Government Accounting Office
Washington, DC 20402
Explains federal benefits.